FLYING *INTO THE* FUTURE

A PICTORIAL HISTORY OF SHORTS

To Sam + Ann. Henley.

FLYING INTO THE FUTURE

A PICTORIAL HISTORY OF SHORTS

MICHAEL DONNE

With best wishes,

Michael Donne

Christmas, 1994.

Good Books

Published in association with Short Brothers PLC
by Good Books (GB Publications Limited)
Lagard Farm, Whitley, Wilts SN12 8RL

ISBN O 946555 29 X

Editor : Graham Tarrant
Jacket and inside design : Design/Section, Frome

Colour separation by Fotographics Ltd,
London and Hong Kong
Made and printed in Great Britain by
BPCC Hazells Ltd, Aylesbury

The publishers are grateful to Imperial Publishing Ltd
for their kind permission to reproduce the cigarette cards
featured on pages 43, 45, 46, 47, 52, 59

The pictures on pages 44 (bottom), 49 (top and bottom
right), 50, 51, 52, 66, 68 are by courtesy of British
Airways Archives; those on pages 81, 137 by courtesy of
Rolls-Royce plc
The picture of Oswald Short on page 14 is from
Quadrant Picture Library

CONTENTS

AUTHOR'S NOTE

To convey to both the knowledgeable aviation enthusiast as well as the general reader the stories of two major industrial organisations several thousand miles apart which, after long and distinguished individual histories of their own, eventually came together, is rather like walking a literary tightrope. There has to be enough historical background to tell the story adequately, yet leaving sufficient room to do justice to the impressive selection of pictures.

The similarities between Horace Short in England and Joseph-Armand Bombardier, the founder of Bombardier in Canada, are remarkable. Although they never met (they were of different generations), both Horace and Joseph-Armand were original thinkers and brilliant inventors, one in aeronautics and the other in motor-traction; whilst both Oswald Short (Horace's younger brother) and Laurent Beaudoin (Joseph-Armand's son-in-law) were obliged by the deaths of their respective seniors to become strong industrial administrators at comparatively early ages, and to carry their separate organisations forward to new heights of achievement. That their two organisations should be joined, through the acquisition of Short Brothers by Bombardier, could never have been foreseen by the founders, but seems set to be beneficial to both groups for many years into the future.

In putting this book together, I have been helped by many people, too numerous to mention individually, on both sides of the Atlantic. To them all I extend my gratitude for their time, patience, generosity and courtesy, with the hope that the result meets with their approval.

MICHAEL DONNE, OBE
OCTOBER 1992

FOREWORD

We are rightly proud of Shorts' history and of our engineering heritage, but as Mark Twain said, "There was worlds of reputation in it, but no money". That finally was the problem.

Since privatisation was completed in 1989, Shorts have come through a process of change more widespread, more fundamental and more complete than any other company I know. Now established within the Bombardier corporate family, we have replaced old with new, slow with fast; we have embraced new ideas and philosophies; sometimes, we barely recognise ourselves!

We know that the future which Shorts are now creating is built on the foundations which previous generations of Shorts people had established, often in a very difficult political and financial environment. Nor should we ignore the vision of those who put the privatisation agreement together, an agreement which has given us new life and a new future.

When change of this magnitude occurs, it inevitably renders existing company histories out-of-date. Shorts are no exception. So we investigated producing an add-on loose-leaf chapter to go with *Pioneers of the Skies*, which we had published in 1987, but concluded that this was an unprofessional and untidy solution. We asked for ideas within the company and that is where the idea for this book came from.

This industry is highly photogenic. I know that other companies have, like us, marvellous archives which go back many decades - in our case right back to the years before the First World War. There are far too many pictures ever to be reproduced in one volume but a large measure of the enjoyment that is derived from looking at them comes from the people, the personalities through the years, who feature in them.

This, then, is a book about change and a book about people: the Shorts people. Michael Donne has woven his own brand of magic in assembling and describing the people, the aircraft, the story, with many of the pictures appearing for the very first time. I thank him for his superb professionalism.

Adlai Stevenson once said that "we can chart our future clearly and wisely only when we know the path which has led to the present". If that is so, then this book will play its part in our future successes.

Today's Shorts people have a lot to be proud of.

ROY McNULTY, CBE
PRESIDENT, SHORT BROTHERS PLC

PART ONE

PIONEERS OF THE SKIES

1897-1989

"I believe we were undoubtedly the first firm to lay down a works and plant purely for the construction of aeroplanes."

OSWALD SHORT

PIONEERS OF THE SKIES

Although Short Brothers were not formally established until November 1908, as a partnership registered in Battersea, London, with a capital of £600, their history effectively began 11 years earlier, in 1897. For in that year one of the three brothers whose names were to become famous in world aviation, having long been interested in ballooning (or "Aerostation" as it was sometimes called), paid £30 for a second-hand passenger-carrying coal-gas balloon called *Queen of the West.*

The brother was Albert Eustace (known always as Eustace), the middle of the three, born in 1875 in Chilton, County Durham, and it was he who really launched the family name in aeronautics. His elder brother, Horace Leonard, born in 1872 at Chilton, was an engineer, at that time adventuring overseas (he had a miraculous escape from cannibals in the South Pacific whilst en route to Australia, and ran a silver mine in Mexico when still only 21); while the youngest, Hugh Oswald, born in 1883 at Stanton-by-Dale in Derbyshire, was swept along as a young and impressionable boy by Eustace's enthusiasm.

Ballooning filled the lives of Eustace and Oswald for more than a decade. Financed by cash earned from Eustace's small London coal merchant's business (started with money given by Horace to help sustain the family whilst he was overseas), they gradually became expert balloon pilots and designed and built their own balloons - first at Hove in Sussex, then in London in a rented mews carriage shed off the Tottenham Court Road, and after that underneath the railway arches in Battersea - enjoying the fame and comparative wealth their exploits conferred on them. (Later they also had a balloon works in Clapham.) In 1906 they won a prize for excellence of balloon construction and became the official balloon makers to the Aero Club, which was formed in 1901 and became the Royal Aero Club on 15 February 1910.

More significantly, however, their ballooning brought them into contact with a small but growing band of other pioneer balloonists who were also to become enthusiasts for powered aviation. This included The Hon. Charles Stewart Rolls, a rich but adventurous aristocrat (the third son of the Lord Llangatock), who also much enjoyed motoring and later became co-founder of Rolls-Royce with Frederick Henry Royce.

It was Oswald who was primarily the driving force for the move into powered fixed-wing flight, sensing that interest in ballooning was slowly fading as the public's craving for excitement was fuelled by the new phenomenon. Oswald convinced Eustace, and then urged Horace to join them.

Horace, long back in England from his overseas adventures had shown no interest in ballooning (he made two flights with Eustace in May and August 1898, the latter with Oswald also aboard, that convinced him his two brothers were mad!). He was by then working for C.A.Parsons in Newcastle on steam-turbine design, having earlier spent some time trying to make money developing a sound-amplification invention of his own called an Auxetophone. The notion of powered flight was much more appealing than steam-turbines. He quit Parsons, returned to London, and the partnership in aircraft manufacture was established.

The three brothers had launched themselves on a flooding tide. Enthusiasm for powered aviation before the First World War was massive, and progress rapid, with much media support and vast prizes offered by newspapers such as the *Daily Mail* which did much to encourage would-be aviation pioneers. Once involved, the three brothers made astonishingly swift progress. Battersea gave way to the Aero Club's flying ground at Leysdown on the Isle of Sheppey, then to nearby Eastchurch, and then, just before the war, to a new purpose-built factory at Rochester on the River Medway - because by this time Short Brothers had become the country's leading pioneers of naval aviation and needed a stretch of uncluttered river for their landings.

The decades that followed were full of extraordinary vigour and inventiveness. The First World War did much to help; but then Horace died suddenly on 6 April 1917, aged only 44, and although Eustace survived until 1932, it was really Oswald who effectively ran the company after Horace's death. He remained at the helm until the sudden government expropriation of the company for alleged inefficiency in 1943, in the dark days of the Second World War.

Those intervening decades, rich in aeronautical endeavour although poor in terms of financial success, saw many designs flowing from Short Brothers, including some of the most famous aeroplanes of all time. They included the great C-Class Empire flying boats - true Queens of the Skies in their day - which in the hands of Imperial Airways helped to forge closer links with home for the outposts of the British Empire. Later came the Sunderland flying boat, which in the Second World War helped to ensure Britain's survival in the fierce anti-submarine Battle of the Atlantic, and in turn led to new classes of flying boats - the Hythes, Sandringhams and Solents used by Imperial's successor, British Overseas Airways Corporation.

Shorts' inventive flair continued even after the government takeover, but the new owner, instead of helping the company to new peaks of success, was not orientated to the commercial world. The post-Second World War years were a long hand-to-mouth struggle for survival in increasingly competitive world markets, without the funding to secure a long-term future.

But they were also years in which Shorts' contribution to aviation development was astonishing. Years which saw their pioneering research into vertical take-off and landing; their inventiveness in guided weapons development with the Seacat and Tigercat and other missiles; their engineering expertise in the evolution of a specialist aerostructures business making components for other companies' aeroplanes; and, especially, their dedication to the development of short-haul regional aviation with such highly successful aeroplanes as the Skyvan, the SD-330 and the SD-360.

The company might have continued in that fashion for many more years - producing many new ideas but making little money under government control - had it not been for another twist of political fate. The successive Conservative governments under the premiership of Margaret Thatcher from 1979 set themselves the task of "rolling back the frontiers of the State" in a massive programme of privatisation - selling back to the private sector assets which had been earlier taken over for various reasons by previous administrations.

The aerospace industry was included in that programme. During the 1980s both British Aerospace and Rolls-Royce were privatised, and in 1988 the Government made it clear that it was looking for buyers for Short Brothers. The Government's view was that the company was of sufficient strength in industrial terms - although not in financial terms, for it had been incurring considerable losses - to be able to survive in the outside world without the protection, such as it was, of government ownership.

The path to privatisation, however, was not an easy one. In the first instance, it became clear that the Government had its own ideas as to how to achieve it, which included the possibility of a direct sale to another major organisation rather than a public flotation of shares on the Stock Exchange. At the same time, it also emerged that while the Government was ready to accept a single buyer for Short Brothers, it would not be averse to selling off parts of the company to different buyers if a single purchaser could not be found.

But Rodney Lund (who had taken over as Chairman, following the retirement of Sir Philip Foreman in 1988) and his team knew only too well that the company's success had been born out of the interdependence of its three major divisions - aircraft, missiles and aerostructures - and that the cross-fertilisation of technical knowledge and skills between them kept the company alive and nourished its technological expertise. To break Shorts up would, in their view, be effectively to destroy it, and thereby destroy the biggest single private sector employer in Northern Ireland, with devastating effects on the province's technological and manufacturing base, in addition to having major political and sociological consequences.

As a result, throughout the last few months of 1988 and the early weeks of 1989, Mr Lund and his colleagues fought one of the toughest battles ever with ministers and civil servants in a bid to ensure that the Government would sell the company only to a single bidder. After much deliberation, on 7 June 1989, just before the opening of the Paris International Air Show, the Government announced that it had selected Bombardier of Canada, a major transportation and industrial group, as the preferred purchaser of Short Brothers. "Heads of agreement" for the

deal had been reached between the Government and the Canadian company, with further detailed discussions to follow, aimed at a formal transfer of ownership to be achieved later that year.

The final sale agreement was signed on 4 October 1989, and Short Brothers was restored to the private sector - "Back where we belong," declared Rodney Lund - after 46 years of government ownership.

Laurent Beaudoin, Chairman and Chief Executive Officer of Bombardier, made it clear at the time that despite Shorts' financial losses, he believed the company had considerable potential. That judgement has subsequently been proved correct, for after only a short time in Bombardier ownership, a revitalised Short Brothers is already demonstrating renewed strength in world markets, and is set to continue making a major contribution to world aerospace into the 21st century.

1. THE BALLOON ENTHUSIASTS

1897-1909

Although the Short brothers' balloon activities carried on well into the second decade of the 20th century, their greatest period of balloon endeavour lasted little more than 10 years. They brought to it such dedication and expertise that they quickly became the foremost balloon designers and manufacturers in Europe, if not in the world, with a flourishing export business for civil and military customers.

The three Short brothers. (Right) Horace (1872-1917), the eldest, had suffered a head injury whilst young which led to meningitis, leaving him with a cranial disfiguration - which he used to great effect to intimidate others. He had a wide mental horizon, a quick wit and a sharp tongue, and his ideas laid the foundations for naval aircraft design in this country.

Hugh Oswald (1883-1969), the youngest, always known as Oswald and initially called "The Kid" by Horace. But in the event he was the one who contributed most to Short Brothers, effectively running the company from 1917 until it was expropriated by the Government in 1943. Even Horace came to respect Oswald's business acumen; after his death in 1917 it was Oswald who took over the supervision of the Shorts' business, with Eustace continuing to look after the balloon (and later) airship side.

Albert Eustace (1875-1932), the middle brother, described as "looking like a dreamy poet", but nonetheless an astute businessman whose initial interest in ballooning launched the three brothers on the path that was to lead to powered aviation.

Horace Short in 1900, aged 28, with his Auxetophone sound-amplifier, which he tested at full amplitude from the top of the Eiffel Tower in Paris, to the fury of many Parisians. He eventually sold his patents in the invention to C.A.Parsons.

Pen drawings by Oswald Short of a balloon and component parts, showing how closely as a young man he identified himself with his brother Eustace's interest in ballooning. Signed by Oswald on the far right.

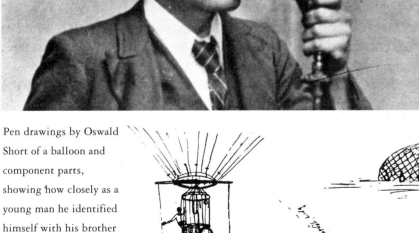

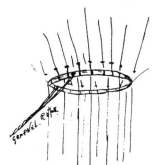

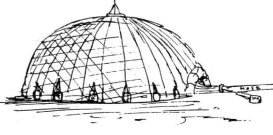

An advertisement of 1898 promoting Short Brothers' balloon activities by illustrating an ascent at Teddington (probably at a Church Temperance Guild Fete on Whit Monday), in which Eustace was accompanied by his brother Horace and another balloon enthusiast, Mr. A. Williams of Battersea. It was that flight, to Otford in Kent, a distance of 40 miles (64km) covered in 45 minutes which convinced Horace that balloons were "nasty, useless and dangerous contraptions", and that his brothers were "mad, balloon mad!" For it was a "rough" flight with the balloon dragging on landing.

(Left) A cutting from the *Daily Mirror* of 26 September 1904, illustrating a Gala Day Ascent at the Crystal Palace in South London ("witnessed by scores of thousands of *Mirror* readers") of a balloon built by the Shorts, and claimed to be the biggest in the world at that time. The small picture top centre shows the balloon soon after release from the ground.

Photographer, Herbert Salmon, Teddington.
BALLOON ASCENT, TEDDINGTON, 1898.

An early photograph, probably around the turn of the century, showing Eustace Short (centre) in front of his balloon *Queen of the West*, with two balloonist friends.

One of the great pioneers of ballooning (and also of motoring and powered flight) was the Hon. Charles Stewart Rolls, the third son of the Lord Llangatock. Tall, slim, elegant, rich and patrician, he was a co-founder of the Aero Club in 1901. In 1906 he joined forces with Frederick Henry Royce to form the motor manufacturing company Rolls-Royce. Rolls did much to foster the Short brothers' early efforts in building aeroplanes. Here he is shown delivering despatches to Boy Scouts by balloon.

(Clockwise from top left) Oswald Short, the Hon. J.T.C. Moore-Brabazon, Griffith Brewer and Eustace Short preparing for a balloon ascent on 25 August 1907.

The Short Brothers balloon works at the Battersea railway arches, close to the gasworks - the source of coal gas for flights (circa 1909). On the left is *Venus*, with *Continental 2* alongside it being prepared for flight. At that time the three brothers were on the verge of their early attempts to build fixed-wing aircraft, but the cash for those endeavours was still earned from their balloon manufacturing activities.

The Short brothers' move into design and manufacture of manned, powered aeroplanes was stimulated by a growing enthusiasm for aviation throughout Europe, following the belated publicity given to the epochal Wright brothers' first powered, sustained and controlled flight in a heavier-than-air machine at Kill Devil Hill, Kitty Hawk, North Carolina, on 17 December 1903. The move was inevitable, for Oswald rightly recognised that public interest in ballooning would never be sustained in the face of powered aviation.

Wilbur (far left) and Orville Wright, the bicycle-makers of Dayton, Ohio, whose achievement of powered flight, initially kept largely unpublicised, slowly percolated through to the outside world. The news triggered a burst of activity among pioneer aviators, in particular in Britain and France, as they strove to emulate and if possible go well beyond the success of the two Americans.

The Shorts' first effort at building aeroplanes had been a glider for J.T.C. Moore-Brabazon in 1907. It was built at the Battersea balloon works but was not a success, because as Oswald said much later, "At that time neither Eustace nor I had given any thought to gliding or aeroplanes". The picture shows the interior of the works at Battersea, with the comparatively crude equipment and machinery used for building early aircraft. Production was virtually all by hand, on a one-off basis for each individual customer.

Wilbur Wright came to Europe in August 1908 to give demonstration and passenger flights in the *Wright Flyer* at Hunaudières Racecourse, near Le Mans, then at nearby Camp d'Auvours, and later still at Pont-Long, near Pau. Many aspiring British aviators visited him and were given flights, including C.S.Rolls, Frank McClean, Griffith Brewer, Frank Hedges Butler and Major B.F.S.Baden-Powell. Their enthusiastic reports led Eustace to make a trip to meet Wilbur. On Wilbur's second visit to France, from 5 December 1908, Eustace went again and was given another flight. He in turn prompted Horace to go, in February 1909, and the latter made this sketch, among others, of the Wrights' design.

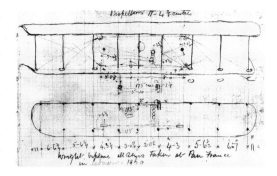

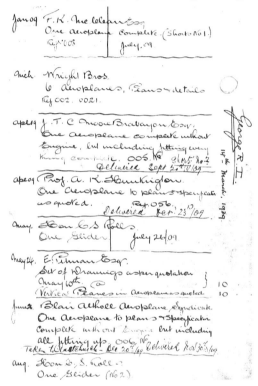

As a result of Horace's visit to France, the Short brothers secured the manufacturing rights to the *Wright Flyer* in England - the Wrights had never seriously considered mass production themselves - and quickly established orders for six aircraft. These are shown listed on the first page of Shorts' very first order book, underneath that for Frank McClean's aircraft (Shorts No. 1). The signature of King George VI was added on the occasion of his visit to Shorts on 14 March 1939. Those first orders justifiably led the Short brothers to call themselves "The First Manufacturers of Aircraft In the World".

It was clearly becoming necessary for the Short brothers to establish a more permanent base for aviation than the Battersea balloon works. They found it in 1909 at Leysdown, a lonely site on the Isle of Sheppey, where a noted aviator (and balloonist) Frank McClean had bought land for an airfield, renting it to the Aero Club for one shilling a year so that members could use it for flying lessons. Writing much later, Oswald confessed that at that time "next to nothing was known in this country of the problems which had to be solved to achieve heavier-than-air flight... we financed our own operations. I believe we were undoubtedly the first firm to lay down a works and plant purely for the construction of aeroplanes." As a result of the move, a steady stream of aeroplane designs began to flow from Horace, who was the head of the firm and chief designer.(Top right) The first factory at Leysdown in 1909; (bottom left) the new factory built at nearby Eastchurch in 1910 as the workload grew; (centre) the Aero Club's sheds and Shorts' works at Eastchurch as they had expanded by 1911.

The most famous line-up of early aviators ever seen, taken in May 1909 at Mussel Manor, the Aero Club's clubhouse at Leysdown, where Oswald lived for some time in the early years. (Standing, left to right) J.D.F.Andrews; Oswald Short; Horace Short; Eustace Short; Frank (later Sir Francis) McClean, Irish mine-owner, astronomer and pioneer aviator, holder of Aero Club Pilot's Certificate No. 11; Griffith Brewer, the Wright brothers' patent agent in the British Empire and President of the Aeronautical Society of Great Britain; Frank Hedges Butler, joint founder of the Aero Club; Dr. W.J.S. Lockyer, an astronomer, balloonist and pioneer of aerial photography; Warwick Wright, motor-racing and aviation pioneer. (Seated, left to right) J.T.C. Moore-Brabazon, later Lord Brabazon of Tara, holder of Aero Club Pilot's Certificate No. 1; Wilbur Wright; Orville Wright; and the Hon. C.S. Rolls.

Following the visits by Eustace and Horace to Wilbur Wright in France, the two Wright brothers came to England and visited the Shorts at Leysdown on 4 May 1909. Here they are seen (Orville on the left, Wilbur on the right) during their inspection of work in progress. Horace Short is on the far left.

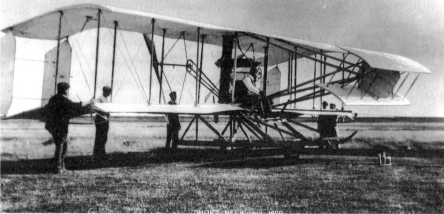

The first really serious attempt at an aircraft was the Short-Wright biplane No.1 - based on Horace's sketches of the Wrights' aeroplane - seen here with Frank McClean on board in August 1909. Ordered in January 1909, it was delivered in July, indicating the time taken to custom-build the machine. But the aircraft was initially unsuccessful, with a flight of only four inches (10cm) off the end of its launching rail because of an underpowered Nordenfelt engine. It was more successful later with a French Bariquand et Marre engine.

Shorts No. 2 Biplane, 1909 (and modified machine, 1910)

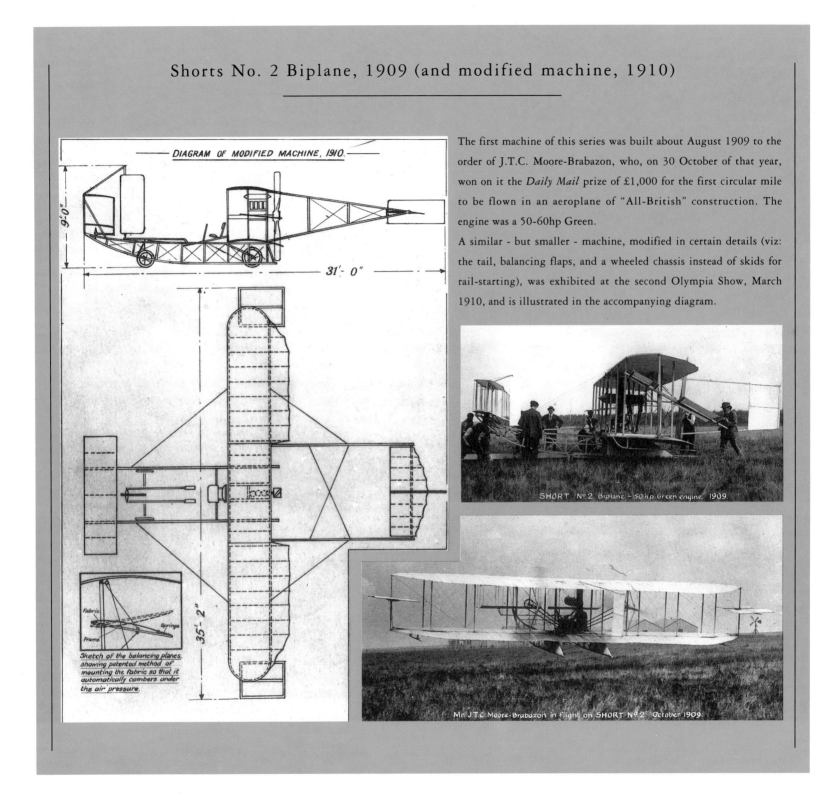

DIAGRAM OF MODIFIED MACHINE, 1910.

9'-0"

31'- 0"

35'-2"

Fabric

Springs

Frame

Sketch of the balancing planes, showing patented method of mounting the fabric so that it automatically cambers under the air pressure.

SHORT Nº 2 Biplane – 50 h.p. Green engine. 1909.

Mr J.T.C. Moore-Brabazon in flight on SHORT Nº 2. October 1909.

The first machine of this series was built about August 1909 to the order of J.T.C. Moore-Brabazon, who, on 30 October of that year, won on it the *Daily Mail* prize of £1,000 for the first circular mile to be flown in an aeroplane of "All-British" construction. The engine was a 50-60hp Green.

A similar - but smaller - machine, modified in certain details (viz: the tail, balancing flaps, and a wheeled chassis instead of skids for rail-starting), was exhibited at the second Olympia Show, March 1910, and is illustrated in the accompanying diagram.

The Short brothers lost no time in publicising themselves, as these two advertisements from *Flight* magazine show. The first (8 October 1910) is modest by comparison with the second (11 February 1911), by which time they had moved from Leysdown to nearby Eastchurch, indicating the growing success of their business.

The move to Eastchurch was significant, for by 1911 the Short brothers had become interested in seaplanes, and Eastchurch was closer to the sea. Shorts had built a twin-Gnome engine aircraft with floats and a land chassis, effectively an amphibian. The floats were air-bags made of canvas lined with rubber balloon fabric. This venture was timely, for the Admiralty had set up an Air Division under Captain Murray Sueter in 1910 (he later became Rear Admiral Sir Murray Sueter and a Member of Parliament) and the first small handful of naval officers learned to fly at Eastchurch. Horace also invented folding wings for seaplanes, enabling them to be stowed aboard ships or in other confined spaces (they also helped in towing the aircraft along the narrow lanes from the factory to the sea!).

SHORT BROS.

Aeroplane & Balloon
- - Manufacturers, - -
LONDON & SHEPPEY.

Sole Manufacturers and Agents in Great Britain & Ireland for

Messrs. Wilbur & Orville Wright.

EARLY DELIVERIES for WRIGHT MACHINES can be given, fitted with both wheels & skids.

BALLOON WORKS
**Battersea & Clapham,
LONDON.**
Telegrams—" Ballooning, London."
Telephone—788 Battersea.

AEROPLANE WORKS:
**Eastchurch & Shellbeach,
SHEPPEY.**
Telegrams—" Flight, Eastchurch."
Telephone—6a Minster-on-Sea.

C.S.Rolls was one of the most enthusiastic flyers at Leysdown, piloting gliders and powered aircraft, as shown in this picture of him aboard a Short-built Wright Flyer at Leysdown. Rolls was subsequently killed in a precision landing mishap at a Bournemouth flying meeting in July 1910, whilst flying a French-built Wright aeroplane which against the advice of his mechanic he had modified himself.

Short Bros.

Aeroplane and Balloon Manufacturers,
LONDON & SHEPPEY.

WRIGHT BIPLANES.
(Wilbur and Orville Wrights' Patents.)

SHORT BIPLANES.
(Prize winners at meetings.) Fitted with SHORT'S PATENT ROLLING GEAR,; DUPLEX CONTROL and SHORT'S PATENT SAFETY WIRE TENSORS. These Machines are **unequalled** for RELIABILITY, SAFETY, and EASE OF CONTROL.

SHORT MONOPLANES,
for one or two persons, fitted with SHORT'S PATENT LANDING CHASSIS and other devices. Of best design and workmanship throughout.

PROPELLERS
supplied of approved design at reasonable prices. Quotations given to purchasers' specifications.

SHORT'S BAROGRAPHS & ANEROIDS
used by leading Aviators.

SHORT'S STATOSCOPE.
Indispensable for high altitudes.

The cost of repairs and renewals to a client who has flown one of our Biplanes nearly 400 miles since it left the factory is less than £1.

Balloon Works:
Battersea & Clapham, London.

Aeroplane Works:
Eastchurch Sheppey.

Over the next few years a steady stream of designs flowed from the Short brothers. The rapidity with which their knowledge and expertise increased is illustrated by these three early aircraft:

(Left) The biplane No. 27 (1910)
(Above) The Triple-Twin biplane (1911)
(Below) The Tandem-Twin biplane (1911)

Shorts 100hp Tractor Biplane, 1912

The 100hp Tractor was designed in 1911, and the first machine made its appearance early in 1912. It was then fitted with a "land" chassis, which was subsequently replaced by floats, and the converted machine - flown with great success by Commander Samson and playing a conspicuous part in the naval manoeuvres of 1912 - became the forerunner of the famous Shorts seaplanes.

Improved machines of this type were used during the early part of the war, and provided three of the squadron of seven Shorts seaplanes which carried out the raid on the German naval base at Cuxhaven on Christmas Day 1914.

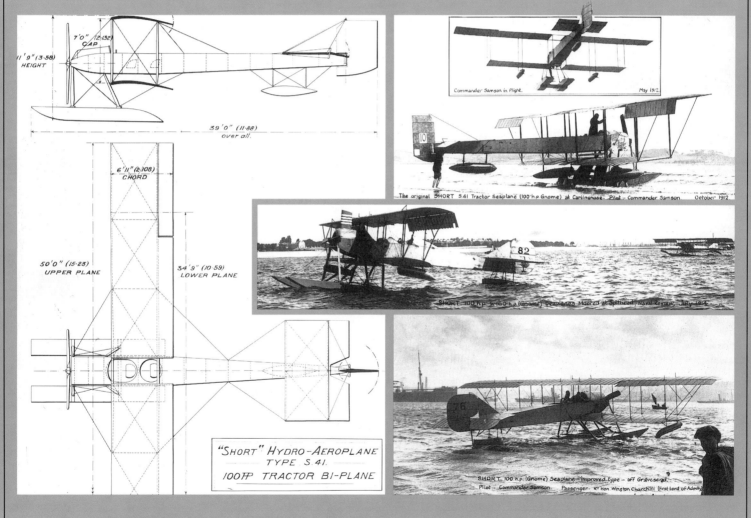

"SHORT" HYDRO-AEROPLANE TYPE S.41. 100HP TRACTOR BI-PLANE

Commander Samson in Flight. May 1912.

The original SHORT S.41 Tractor Seaplane (100 h.p. Gnome) at Carlingnose. Pilot:- Commander Samson. October 1912.

SHORT 100 h.p. & 160 h.p. (Gnome) Seaplanes Moored at Spithead. Naval Review, July 1914.

SHORT. 100 h.p. (Gnome) Seaplane - Improved type - off Gravesend. Pilot - Commander Samson. Passenger:- Rt Hon. Winston Churchill (First Lord of Admty)

Shorts Hydro-Aeroplane - Flight up the Thames to London, 1912

On Saturday, 10 August 1912, Frank McClean flew up the Thames on his Shorts biplane - a machine of the "Modified S-27" Type fitted with floats. Starting from Harty Ferry, Isle of Sheppey, he followed the coast to Sheerness, and continued up the Thames to Westminster, passing under various bridges en route. The return journey, on the following day, was not so successful, owing to the imposition of police restrictions against rising from the water, and in endeavouring to take off at the point indicated by the police, McClean damaged a float, the machine being returned to Eastchurch by road. This occasion was the first on which a hydro-aeroplane had been flown in London.

A major achievement in the development of naval aviation was the first flight off a ship's deck by a modified Shorts S-27 fitted with air-bags. The aircraft took off from a platform on HMS *Africa*, a 15,740-ton battleship at anchor, on 10 January 1912. The pilot was Commander Charles Samson, one of the first naval officers to fly. In May, he repeated the performance with an S-38 from a moving warship, the 15,785-ton cruiser HMS *Hibernia*, steaming at 10½ knots (19.5km/h) off Portland as part of the Weymouth Naval Review. He landed on the ground at Lodmoor outside Weymouth. Another aircraft, S- 41, was also aboard *Hibernia*, but was lowered into the water and flown away as a seaplane. Following the Review, the Admiralty ordered 25 new seaplanes, mostly to be built by Shorts.

(Clockwise from top right) Preparing HMS *Hibernia* prior to the flight; the S-38 being hoisted aboard; the aircraft taking off at sea; Commander Samson back on land; the special staging on the *Hibernia's* deck.

Commander Samson flying the S-38 over the Royal Yacht at the 1912 Weymouth Naval Review.

By 1913 virtually all of Shorts' work was on seaplanes for the Admiralty, and because of the growing use of Eastchurch for naval activities, the company needed a site for another, bigger, factory. It was found on the River Medway at Rochester,

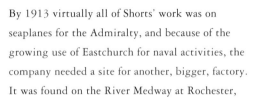

SHORT BROS' WORKS AT ROCHESTER, 1915.

with a clear stretch of river for take-offs and landings, and a plentiful supply of labour. The new factory was built between October 1913 and January 1914, and was in full production when war broke out a few months later. The picture shows an early view of the Rochester works, which later was considerably expanded.

Winston Churchill became First Lord of the Admiralty in Autumn 1911, and gave considerable support to the evolution of naval aviation. He is seen here (circa 1914) as a passenger in the rear seat of a Shorts Tractor biplane, piloted by Commander Samson, at the Royal Naval Air Station on the Isle of Grain. The 100hp Tractor biplane, designed in 1911 as a landplane, later fitted with floats, was the ancestor of all Shorts seaplanes and flying boats, although the basic design obviously underwent many subsequent changes.

Shorts Hydro-Aeroplane - Flight up the Nile, 1914

The first waterplane to be flown up the River Nile was a 160hp "Short" piloted by Frank McClean, who commenced the flight at Alexandria on 3 January 1914 and continued, by various stages, to Khartoum. He was accompanied by Horace Short, Alec Ogilvie and Dr Norman Lockyer. The machine was a Gnome-engined "pusher" biplane fitted with floats, weighing - with 37 gallons (168 litres) of fuel and a crew of four - about 1.6 tonnes, and having a speed, when fully loaded, of about 72mph (116km/h). The wings had a chord and gap of five feet (1.52m), a span of 67 feet (20.42m), and were constructed on the Shorts patent folding principle.

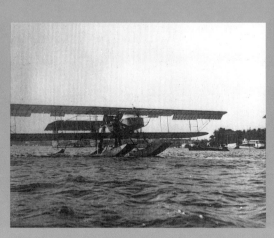

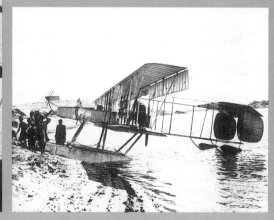

1914-1918

The war offered Shorts a great opportunity to develop their expertise across the entire spectrum of manned powered flight, as the demand for improved performance encouraged innovation in design, and mass production techniques were introduced to build bigger and more powerful aircraft.

The Type 310 was a variant of the Shorts model 166 two-seat biplane, also with a Canton-Unné engine, of 1915. It was used for torpedo attack and training.

Shorts Seaplanes - 135hp and 200hp Canton-Unné, 1914

The Shorts 200hp (Canton-Unné) seaplane was designed about the end of 1913, the first machine being produced early in 1914. It carried a torpedo slung between the main floats, and was one of the earliest machines to be fitted with the Shorts patent folding wings, the 160hp Gnome being actually the first to be so fitted.

One of these machines took part in the raid on Cuxhaven on Christmas Day 1914, the remainder of the squadron of seven Shorts seaplanes comprising three of the 100-Gnome type, two 160-Gnome, and one of the 135hp Canton-Unné type, which were similar in design to the 200hp machines but on a smaller scale, no torpedo being carried.

SHORT 200 h.p (Canton-Unne) SEAPLANE 1914

SHORT 200 h.p (Canton-Unne) SEAPLANE

SHORT 135 h.p (Canton-Unne) Seaplane

SHORT 135 h.p (Canton-Unne) Seaplane

SHORT 135 h.p (C-U.) SEAPLANE

Shorts 250hp (Rolls-Royce) Bombing Aeroplane, 1916

The Shorts 250hp aeroplane was one of the earliest "big bombers" to be used in the war. Its span was 85ft (25.9m), overall length 45ft (13.7m), height 15ft (4.57m), chord 6ft (1.83m) and gap 6ft 3in (1.9m). Its offensive equipment consisted of machine gun and four 230lb (104kg) bombs - or, alternatively, eight 112lb (51kg) bombs.

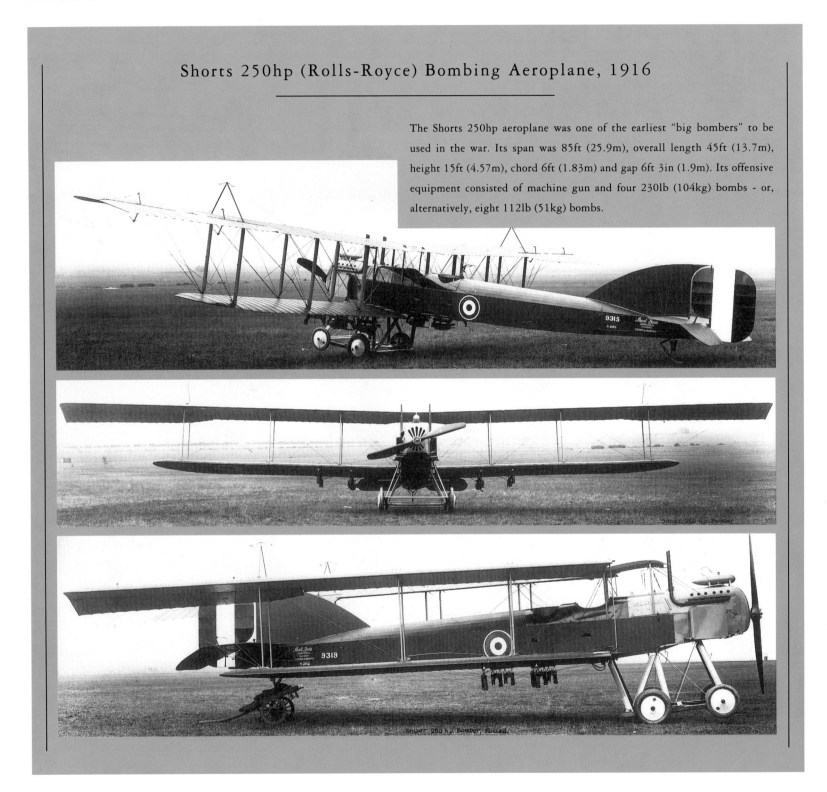

The Admiralty Type 184 two-seat torpedo, bombing and patrol aircraft was one of Shorts' most important wartime designs, with close to 1,000 aircraft being built in various versions by both Shorts itself (115) and other companies (nearly 850). Some remained in service with foreign air forces until 1933, a tribute to the versatility of the design. Oswald Short was always bitter about the way in

which the Admiralty, in order to boost production, ordered him to pass the designs over to other companies, including rivals such as Fairey Aviation and Saunders of Cowes, who remained in business after the war. Oswald said, "Short Brothers can claim to have hatched these chickens which have proved not an unmixed blessing so far as competition is concerned." The aircraft shown here was built by Phoenix Dynamo (later to become part of English Electric).

The Scout N-2A No.1 experimental bombing seaplane made its maiden flight on 23 January 1917. It was the last design by Horace, "The Father of the Seaplane", who died of a cerebral haemorrhage on 6 April after a few days' illness, at the early age of 44. Oswald, then 34, was elevated to the task of running the company, with Eustace continuing to look after the remnants of the balloon business and the newly developing airship activities. Neither the N-2A, nor a later N-2B designed by Oswald himself, won Admiralty contracts and so never went into quantity production.

The wartime head of naval aviation, Murray Sueter (writing in 1928), described Horace as "a great loss to air development, as by the gifts of the Gods, he was a creative genius...he was almost uncanny in his knowledge of what a machine could do, even in its design stages. I never knew him wrong."

The greatest of many great test pilots for Shorts was John Lankester Parker, who joined the company at Eastchurch in 1916, became Chief Test Pilot in 1918 (on the retirement of Ronald Kemp, their first test pilot) and held that post until he retired in 1946; an astonishing 30 years of service. His aeronautical expertise was so great that it was said he could tell from just looking at an aeroplane whether it would fly successfully - and he was never proved wrong. He was the pilot on the maiden flights of every Shorts aircraft from the Shirl of the First World War through to 1943, when he took over administrative duties. After Horace's death in 1917, and even more so after that of Eustace in 1932, Oswald came to rely heavily on Parker's judgement, preferring it even to the views of chief designers and other senior personnel.

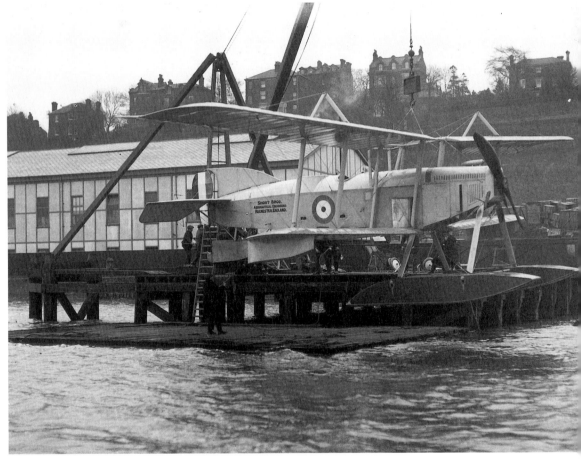

Shorts Seaplanes - 275hp Sunbeam, Type N/2B, 1917

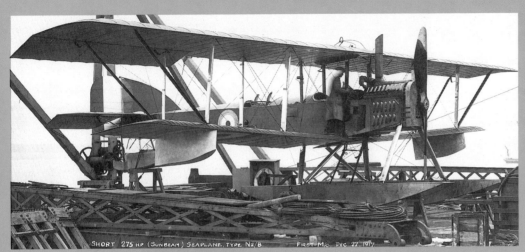

SHORT 275 HP (SUNBEAM) SEAPLANE. TYPE N2/B.   FIRST M/c. Dec 22. 1917.

The N-2B had its uses, although never built in quantity. One famous occasion was on 9 April 1919 when it conveyed Major-General J.E.B. Seely, then Under-Secretary of State for Air, from Rochester to Westminster, landing on the River Thames by Westminster Bridge. Initially with a Sunbeam 275hp Maori I engine, it was underpowered, but when fitted with a Rolls-Royce Eagle VIII performed well. These pictures show the N-2B in various poses, with a view (bottom left) of it landing on the Thames by the House of Commons.

SECOND M/c.

M/c suspended from crane.

SHORT 275 HP SEAPLANE
Conveying General Seely - Under Sec'y For Air -
from Rochester to the House of Commons 9/4/19

View showing underside of floats.

In 1916, during the airship raids by Germany on Britain, Shorts told the Government that it could build rigid airships comparable to the German Zeppelin Class. Its offer was accepted and it erected the Cardington Airship Works in Bedfordshire, where it began work on four such craft - R-31, R-32, R-37 and R-38 - based on an original Vickers rigid airship design. R-31 (pictured here) was launched in August 1918, initially with six Rolls-Royce 250hp Eagle engines, later with five. It only

Things did not always go well! A Shorts floatplane is shown being recovered after a crash.

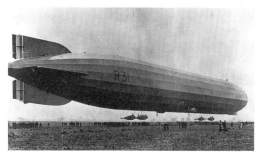

flew for nine hours before being scrapped. The sister craft, R-32, was more successful, flying for 260 hours between 1919 and 1921. It was later deliberately destroyed in a controlled experiment. R-37 was never completed; and R-38 was taken over, together with the works, by the Government for the British Airship Service. R-38 eventually broke up in the air while on a test flight. Shorts were not to blame. "The Admiralty designed the ships," said Oswald, "our men only did the detailed design according to their Admiralty instructions."

An interior view of the Airship Works at Cardington. Shorts set up a small township nearby to house workers, called Shortstown. The airship venture was a major operation, obliging the Short brothers to reconstruct their own company, re-registering it as Short Brothers (Rochester and Bedford), with Oswald as Chairman, and himself and Eustace as Joint Managing Directors. Eustace took over the airship side, leaving Oswald to concentrate on aircraft.

The sheds were eventually commandeered by the Government under the Defence of the Realm Act, for work on its own ill-fated R-101 giant airship, which was destroyed on crashing in a storm near Beauvais in France whilst on its maiden voyage to India on 5 October 1930.

After losing Cardington, Shorts ended all airship work. Oswald fought hard for compensation, eventually winning only £40,000, far less than the company had spent.

in 1917: it had become surrounded by a huge collection of government aircraft hangars, and was in the way of the Admiralty's own naval aviation development plans. The balloon works at Battersea and Clapham had long since gone, and from 1917 onwards Shorts was to make Rochester its home. The River Medway was to see many more famous aircraft take to the skies, until the mid-1930s when the armaments build-up for the Second World War obliged the company to seek additional factory space. This resulted in the opening of the Belfast works in 1936, which operated in parallel with Rochester until the latter itself was abandoned in October 1948.

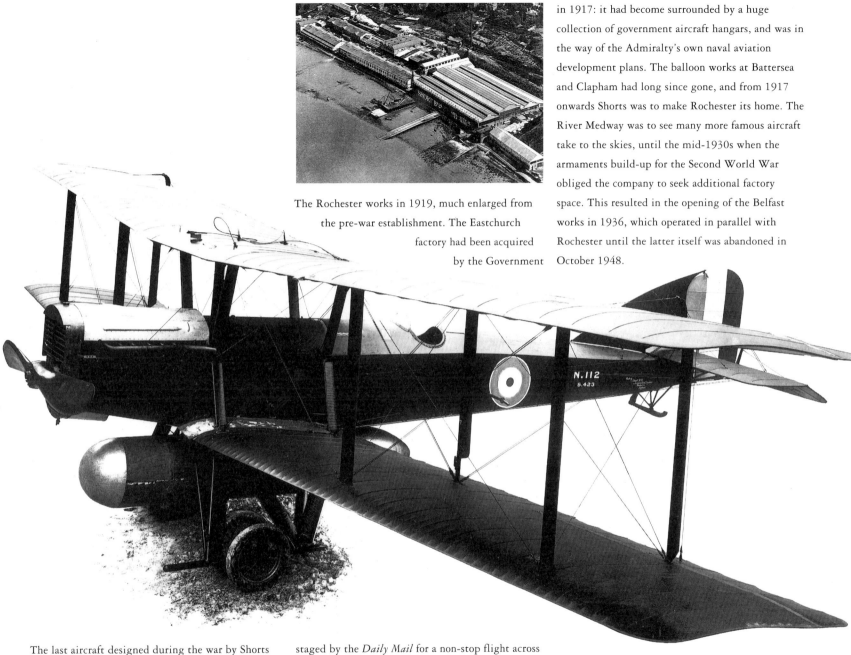

The Rochester works in 1919, much enlarged from the pre-war establishment. The Eastchurch factory had been acquired by the Government

The last aircraft designed during the war by Shorts (late 1918) was the Shirl, originally intended as a torpedo carrier. Shorts redesigned it as a mail carrier, with the mail-container slung under the fuselage. It gave rise to the Shamrock, called the S-538 Atlantic by Shorts, intended as an entrant in a competition staged by the *Daily Mail* for a non-stop flight across the North Atlantic. But the Shamrock was damaged in a mishap en route from England to Ireland, and the £10,000 prize was won by John Alcock and Arthur Whitten-Brown in the Vickers Vimy.

4. BETWEEN THE WARS : THE STRUGGLE FOR SURVIVAL

1919-1939

After the Armistice of 1918, Short Brothers, in common with many other aircraft companies, were faced with the cancellation of outstanding orders, creating a situation of great uncertainty. Production slumped in the industry and managements, desperate for work, were forced to cut back on labour sharply. While Shorts retained some work for the Admiralty and the RAF, for example on the F-5 flying boats, it was obliged to turn to other activities - building bus bodies, barges, motor-boats - as a means of survival. As a result, by 1920 Oswald could claim that he still had as many men working for him as he had at the end of the war. But it was the start of a long and difficult period which only began to turn round in the early 1930s.

Production of motor-boats helped to keep part of the Rochester works busy in the early post-war period. Above is the motor-launch *Discovery*, built for Oswald Short, and launched on 17 August 1920.

Building motor-bus bodies for the London General Omnibus Company and other transport concerns was one way of generating income and maintaining employment. Shorts' production of these ran into several thousands, lasting well into the 1930s. Double-decker trams were also being built, and later trolley-buses as well. Other smaller items that kept Shorts active included the manufacture of car bodies, water-skimmers, flat-irons, steel moulds for accumulators, bus conductors' ticket punches, and even perambulators and children's pedal-cycles.

(Below) Shorts' first aircraft after the war was the Shrimp, a utility sporting seaplane, which made its maiden flight on 10 December 1919. But austerity was all around and only three Shrimps were ever built, one going for survey work in New Guinea and Australia in 1922-23, the other two being broken up.

Shorts pioneered the evolution of all-metal aircraft, with their Silver Streak biplane, which flew on 20 August 1920. It was bought by the Air Ministry for £6,000, for destruction tests. Pilots who flew it liked it, but the Air Ministry placed no orders. Nevertheless, Shorts learned much from it that was to be of value later in the inter-war years.

(Above) Another early post-war activity was the construction of a small number of anti-submarine and general reconnaissance flying boats, developed from a design originating from Squadron-Commander John C. Porte of the Admiralty's Felixstowe Marine Aircraft Experimental Establishment, known as Felixstowe or F-boats. One, sold to Portugal, is seen on the Rochester launching ramp on 28 April 1920.

The Silver Streak led on to the S-3 Springbok of 19 April 1923, designed to meet an Air Ministry specification for a Bristol Fighter replacement. Two were built and bought by the Air Ministry, but there was no quantity production. Note the car chassis in the background awaiting bodies built by Shorts.

The N-3 Cromarty flying boat of 1921 was one of the most advanced designs of its day, and was Shorts' first indigenous

The Mussel I was named after Mussel Manor on Shorts' first flying ground on the Isle of Sheppey, where Oswald had lived for a time in the early days of the company. It was a light two-seat experimental trainer. It first flew on 6 April 1926, but was destroyed in a mishap in August 1928 when Eustace collided with a barge whilst landing in the Medway. It was followed by the Mussel II in May 1929, and it was whilst landing that aircraft that Eustace died of a heart attack, on 8 April 1932. He was 57. His death left Oswald to carry on alone as sole Managing Director of the company, at the age of 49.

venture into pure flying boats (as opposed to seaplanes). Intended as an anti-submarine patrol and bombing aircraft, with two Rolls-Royce Condor engines, it won no orders and only the one prototype was built. But Shorts learned much in designing it, which was to help later as their flying-boat business expanded.

The Crusader single-seat racing seaplane of 4 May 1927 was intended for the Schneider Trophy Race of that year, but it crashed after taking off in Venice Lagoon because of incorrect aileron rigging. The race was won for Britain, however, by Flight Lieutenant S.N.Webster, flying a Supermarine S-5 at 273.07mph (439km/h).

It was around this time that Arthur Gouge began to make his name felt in the company on the design side. He had joined Shorts in 1915 as a workman on the benches, and rose to be a charge-hand, then a foreman. He spent his spare time studying engineering, and took his Bachelor of Science degree at London University. He was a first-class mathematician, and through the technical side of the company eventually rose to become Technical Director, playing a major role in all the company's subsequent aircraft up to 1943. For some reason Oswald took a dislike to him, but found him indispensable. When the Government took over Short Brothers in 1943, Gouge was forced to resign. He went to the Saunders (afterwards Saunders-Roe) company on the Isle of Wight and later designed the giant Princess flying boat, receiving a knighthood for his efforts.

PLAYER'S CIGARETTES

SHORT "SINGAPORE III" FLYING BOAT

The mould of Air Ministry disdain for Shorts' designs was effectively broken with the development of the Singapore, the company's first long-range flying boat. The first version, Singapore I, made its maiden flight on 17 August 1926, but it was not until the Singapore III of 15 June 1934 that Shorts achieved the breakthrough they needed. Some 37 IIIs were built for the RAF during the 1930s, serving at home, in Singapore, the Mediterranean and in the Middle East. Nineteen were still in service on the outbreak of the Second World War in 1939.

There were signs as the 1920s came to a close that the tide might well be turning in favour of Shorts' flying boats. The S-8 Calcutta, a three-engined craft which made its maiden flight on 15 February 1928, found immediate success with Imperial Airways, which ordered two at £18,000 each (Shorts built them for £8,000 apiece!), and then three more at £20,000 each. Oswald later declared: "That was how we made contact with Imperial Airways, and that finally led to the Empire flying boats." The aircraft remained in service until 1936-37, when the remaining three (two having been lost on operational flying) went to Air Service Training at Hamble. Six of the military version of the Calcutta, called the Rangoon, were ordered by the Air Ministry. The aircraft was also bought by the French Government and French Navy, while Louis Breguet built its own derivative, the Bizerte.

The Air Ministry loaned its Rolls-Royce Condor-powered Singapore I flying boat from November 1927 to June 1928 for a major survey flight of 23,000 miles (37,000km) around Africa, sponsored by Sir Charles Wakefield and flown by the famous aviator, Sir Alan Cobham. The aim was to study the possibilities of Cobham and his associates setting up an airline of their own. But in the event, Cobham's plans were pre-empted by Imperial Airways. This commemorative map of the venture is signed by Sir Alan, his wife Gladys, and Oswald Short.

A picture of Winston Churchill MP (as he then was) in the cockpit of a Calcutta flying boat. Oswald is in the background, and on the right is Lankester Parker, Shorts' Chief Test Pilot.

(Below) The S-11 Valetta of 21 May 1930, a three-engined passenger monoplane, was intended to determine if monoplanes were better than biplanes in flying boats. Only one was built. It was used by Sir Alan Cobham in 1931 on another survey flight of the Nile and Central Africa, formally on behalf of Imperial Airways, before being converted to a landplane configuration and used as a test-bed by the Air Ministry.

Satyrus was one of three flying boats built by Shorts for the Imperial Airways' route between England and India, specifically the section between Mirabella (Eastern Crete) and Alexandria (Egypt). Although close to the earlier three-engined Calcutta flying boats, these new aircraft (designated S-17 or Kent Class) were bigger, with four engines each and carrying up to 15 passengers in addition to mail. They were named *Scipio*, *Sylvanus* and *Satyrus*. Built during 1930-31, they entered service in 1931. *Sylvanus* was destroyed by fire in 1935, and *Scipio* sank the following year. *Satyrus* continued successfully until finally being retired in 1938. (Left) All three Kent Class flying boats of Imperial Airways at Alexandria. *Satyrus* is in the foreground.

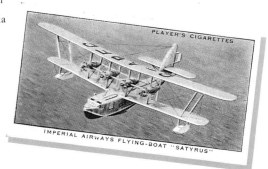

PLAYER'S CIGARETTES

IMPERIAL AIRWAYS LINER "SCYLLA"

PLAYER'S CIGARETTES

PREPARING LUNCH IN IMPERIAL AIRWAYS LINER "SCYLLA"

An even bigger aircraft than the Kent Class was the six-engined S-14 Sarafand patrol and reconnaissance flying boat of 30 June 1932 - in its day the second largest aircraft in the world after the German Dornier Do-X, a 12-engined 150-passenger monster. But it was very costly - £80,000 excluding engines and equipment - and only one was bought by the Air Ministry.

PLAYER'S CIGARETTES

SHORT "SYRINX"

(Left) In 1933 Imperial Airways sought new landplanes for its Western European services, and turned to Shorts when Handley Page, whose HP-42s were used by the airline at that time, quoted excessive prices. Shorts responded swiftly with a landplane design based on the Kent Class flying boats, but with a larger fuselage for 38 passengers.

Designated S-17L and named *Scylla* and *Syrinx*, the two aircraft were completed and tested in time for services to Paris and other cities by mid-1934. Although damaged in a gale at Brussels in late 1935, *Syrinx* was repaired and re-engined and continued in service until being retired in 1940. *Scylla* was destroyed when overturned in a gale in April 1940.

Following the Sarafand, Shorts turned their attention to monoplanes, with the S-16 Scion, a twin-engined, high-wing light transport for five passengers. The first Shorts' passenger monoplane, it flew on 18 August 1933. Five more were built, with Shorts

PLAYER'S CIGARETTES

SHORT "SCION"

themselves using them for internal UK passenger services between Rochester Airport and Southend in the summer of 1934. An improved model, the S-22 Scion II, followed. Ten production aircraft were built, some of which were still in service into the 1960s. An elegant floatplane version, the four-engined S-22 Scion Senior, for 10 passengers, flew on 22 October 1935.

Between the Scion and Scion II, yet another experimental aircraft emerged, the twin-engined S-18 Knuckleduster of 30 November 1933, with a unique gull-winged design, intended to meet an Air Ministry specification for a general purpose and reconnaissance flying boat. But again Shorts lost out to their competitors and no orders were placed.

It was at this stage, with Air Ministry work so sparse, that Shorts realised their immediate future lay with Imperial Airways, which had come a long way in opening up the Empire air routes since its formation by the Government on 31 March 1924. Shorts won their greatest breakthrough with an order from the airline in 1934 "off the drawing board" (with no prototype - an immense gesture of confidence in Shorts) for an initial 14 flying boats, later increased to 28. The order was worth £1.75 million, a massive sum in those days. Three more were ordered by the recently formed Qantas Empire Airways of Australia.

Designated the S-23 or C-Class boats (their names all beginning with C), Imperial Airways called them "Imperial Flying Boats"; but the popular name was "Empire" flying boats. The aircraft were intended to help Imperial Airways open up the Empire air mail and passenger routes to a greater extent than ever before. Each would initially carry 24 passengers and one and a half tons of mail, later changed to 17 passengers and two tons of mail because of the success of the cheap-rate Empire mail scheme. Later, another nine Empire boats were built, the S-30s, for longer distance flights, with four of them being given in-flight refuelling equipment.

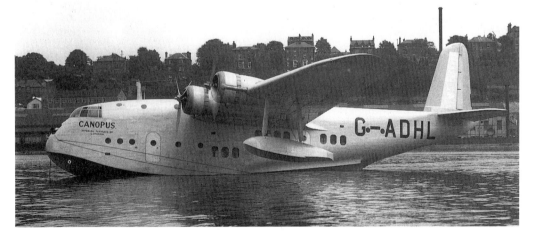

(Clockwise from top right):
A cutaway model of the C-Class Empire flying boat, showing how the passengers, freight and mail were accommodated.
The passenger section of one of the C-Class boats.
The radio officer's position on board.
The first boat, *Canopus*, on the River Medway after launching, 2 July 1936
C-Class flying boats in production at Rochester, July 1936.

The most luxurious Flying-Boat in the world

Length 88ft. • Height from water line 24ft. • Speed 200 M.P.H. (Approx.)
Span 114ft. • Weight fully loaded nearly 18 tons • Crew 5 : Accommodation 24 passengers on day stages and 16 on night journeys
The Empire Flying-Boat—28 are now being built for

IMPERIAL AIRWAYS

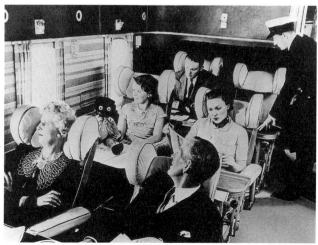

Later, when British Overseas Airways Corporation took over from Imperial Airways, extensive advertising of the flying-boat service was undertaken, as these two posters of the 1940s show.

B·O·A·C

it's a small world by

SPEEDBIRD

Two C-Class flying
boats of Imperial
Airways, *Coriolanus* and
Cambria, moored at
Southampton.

(Right) *Caledonia*, the second of the famous C-Class Empire flying boats, came off the stocks at Rochester on 11 September 1936. It was one of two C-Class boats fitted with extra fuel tanks (*Cambria* was the other) for experimental transatlantic crossings in preparation for a planned joint Imperial Airways-Pan American North Atlantic air service.

Caledonia flew between Foynes in Ireland and Botwood, Newfoundland, on 5/6 July 1937, in 15 hours 9 minutes. It then flew on to Montreal and New York. The aircraft was still in service in 1940, when it was handed over to the newly formed BOAC.

Yet another major development was the Short-Mayo composite flying-boat venture Maia-Mercury, intended to find an alternative to in-flight refuelling for long-distance aircraft, especially over the oceans. The scheme, devised by Major R.H.Mayo, involved using a smaller flying boat (Mercury) that could be launched off the top of a larger "mother" boat (Maia), thereby extending the distance flown to some 3,500 miles (5,600km), or transatlantic range. The Air Ministry ordered the two aircraft from Short Brothers on behalf of Imperial Airways. Maia made its maiden flight on 27 July 1937, Mercury on 5 September 1937. The first joint flight was on 20 January 1938, and the first in-flight separation on 6 February. Flight trials conducted with Captain D.C.T.Bennett of Imperial Airways (later to

be head of the wartime Pathfinder bomber force and then Chairman of British South American Airways) were successful. On one flight Mercury flew from Dundee, Scotland, to the Orange River in South Africa, a distance of 5,997.5 miles (9,652km) in 42 hours 5 minutes, setting a new world distance record for seaplanes. But by then war was looming, and the plan was abandoned. Both Maia and Mercury were later briefly used separately on war duties, Mercury being scrapped in 1941, and Maia being destroyed by enemy action in Poole Harbour the same year.

Mercury is shown here leaving Maia during a test flight. The attachment for the smaller aircraft can be seen on the upper fuselage of Maia.

Just before the Second World War Shorts were exploring monoplane land-based airliners, as these models of four-engined designs show. But war intervened and the aircraft were never built.

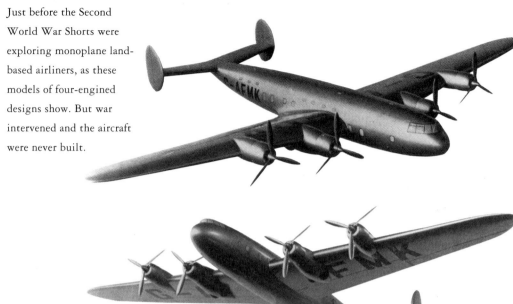

The last commercial flying boats to be built by Shorts immediately prior to the outbreak of the Second World War were the three S-26 G-Class aircraft. These were enlarged and improved versions of the Empire boats, specifically intended for North Atlantic operations. The first, *Golden Hind*, made its maiden flight on 21 July 1939, followed by *Grenadier* and *Grenville* (later renamed *Golden Fleece* and *Golden Horn*). *Golden Hind* was delivered to Imperial Airways, but taken over by the RAF for military duties. The other two were also commandeered. *Golden Fleece* was lost in June 1940, but *Golden Hind* and *Golden Horn* went to BOAC (Imperial Airways' successor) in 1942 as 40-passenger transports flying out of Poole. *Golden Horn* was lost at Lisbon in early 1943, but *Golden Hind* remained with BOAC until sold in September 1947. The picture shows *Golden Hind* on the slipway prior to launching.

5. SECOND WORLD WAR AND GOVERNMENT TAKEOVER

1939-1945

The Second World War cast its shadow long before the outbreak of hostilities, with Short Brothers becoming increasingly involved from around 1936 in preparations which included the manufacture of aircraft designed by other companies, as well as work on their own indigenous designs - the Stirling bomber and the famous Sunderland flying boats.

As part of the build-up, Shorts had established a new factory at Queen's Island, Belfast, in 1936. It had become clear that land restrictions meant the Rochester works was incapable of further expansion, and might also be liable to heavy bombing in wartime being in the vulnerable southeast. After a long search, Belfast was chosen because it offered both a land aerodrome and water for flying boats.

But the pressures of the vast build-up in aircraft activity put great strains on Shorts, and especially on Oswald, which multiplied as the war dragged on, eventually leading to the unprecedented expropriation of the company by the Government on 23 March 1943, when Sir Stafford Cripps was Minister for Aircraft Production. Oswald was effectively dismissed, although given the meaningless title of Honorary President, with no further involvement beyond that date. The company continued, however, under a new, tougher management.

Sunderlands were still in production at Belfast even after the European war was over, as shown in this picture taken in June 1945.

PLAYER'S CIGARETTES

SHORT "SUNDERLAND" FLYING BOAT

Preparations for war began at Shorts in the mid-1930s, with the design of what was to become one of its most famous and successful aircraft - the Sunderland flying boat. Designed by Arthur Gouge, who drew on all his experience with the Empire boats, it was a classic conception which went into many variants, both military and civil, with nearly 750 being built. The aircraft was manufactured at Rochester and at Shorts' new Belfast factory, where it would be less exposed to enemy attack. The first Sunderland flew from Rochester on 16 October 1937.

The Bristol Bombay order was reduced to enable Shorts to concentrate on another sub-contract, production of the Handley Page Hereford twin-engined bomber and crew trainer. The first Shorts-built Hereford flew at Belfast in May 1939, entering squadron service in 1940.

In addition to Sunderlands, Shorts were also building other companies' aircraft, so heavy were the demands made on the aircraft industry in the preparations for war. One was the Bristol Bombay twin-engined bomber and transport, which first flew on 23 July 1935. Bristol became too busy with its own heavy programme on the new Blenheim bomber, so Bombay production was sub-contracted to Shorts at Belfast. Fifty were built there (out of 80 ordered). The picture (left) shows Bombays in the erecting shop in 1939.

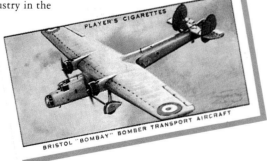

PLAYER'S CIGARETTES

BRISTOL "BOMBAY" BOMBER TRANSPORT AIRCRAFT

Herefords in production at Belfast in August 1939, just before the outbreak of war.

Sunderland flying boats moored against the background of the neighbouring Harland and Wolff shipyard in Belfast.

Shorts' own contribution to the war effort, apart from the Sunderland, was the Stirling four-engined heavy bomber. The first prototype (S-29) flew at Rochester on 14 May 1939 (a half-scale model had flown in 1938, providing much valuable information), but was severely damaged on landing as a result of the undercarriage collapsing. The second prototype flew on 3 December 1939. The aircraft entered service in August 1940, and bore the brunt of the Bomber Command workload until the emergence of the Handley Page Halifax and Avro Lancaster.

The wisdom of spreading the production load through different factories to avoid bombing did not always work. This picture shows severe damage to the Stirling erection bay at Belfast after a raid in 1941. But, in all, 2,299 of the three bomber versions were built, at Belfast, Rochester and at an Austin factory at Birmingham (with main components being supplied by many other companies). Another 160 of a special transport version were also produced.

Shorts ran an advertising campaign in the early stages of the war to promote knowledge of the company's activities, and to pay tribute to the contribution their aircraft were making. Two of the advertisements from *Flight* magazine: (21 November 1940) The exploits of an RAF Sunderland flying boat. (30 November 1941) Prime Minister Winston Churchill on a visit to a Stirling bomber base.

18 1940

ENEMY SAVED BY R.A.F. PILOT

SIGNAL TO ITALIAN HOSPITAL SHIP

SEQUEL TO AJAX ACTION

An interesting sequel to the sinking of three Italian [ ] by H.M.S. Ajax in the Medit[ ] can now be disclosed. [ ] News Service. [ ] way to [ ] ing-bo[ ] sinking [ ] age, [ ] pilo[ ]

The pilot of the Sunderland, a flight lieutenant, said: ". We were on patrol at 8 a.m. when we saw smoke on the horizon on our starboard bow. I altered course to investigate and saw what at first appeared to be a merchant ship. I went round and then gradually closed on the vessel, which we recognized as a hospital ship. We came in close and saw that she was the Aquileia, and then went off. Two or three miles away we saw ship's floats and other objects in the water. We signalled to the hospital ship. Ship's floats and dived two or three times to direct attention, and I few minutes later I saw the hospital ship alter course and lower a white dinghy, which set out in the direction of the floats. We circled round, looking for survivors. We could not definitely see any, though there were many objects the oil which might have been men. Later, resumed our patrol."

GERMANS ADMIT LO OF WA[ ]

Tribute to the
SUNDERLAND

The means and the man
SHORT STIRLING

The biggest and most ambitious flying boat built by Shorts was the Shetland. The S-35 Shetland I and S-40 Shetland II were initially developed to meet the RAF's requirement for a follow-on aircraft to the Sunderland. But delays due to changes of mind, and continuing success with Sunderland variants, caused the RAF to downgrade its requirement and eventually only the two aircraft were built. The Shetland I first flew on 14 December 1944, but was destroyed by fire at its mooring at Felixstowe on 28 January 1946. The second Shetland flew on 17 September 1947; but by then the war was over and the RAF decided it no longer wanted the aircraft. It was offered to BOAC, who declined it, and then used as an engine test-bed until being broken up in 1951.

6. THE INNOVATIVE YEARS

1945-1969

After the war, Shorts might have expected to be given favoured treatment within the aircraft industry, having been taken over by the Government. Instead, things went the other way. Not only was the company not returned to its rightful owners after the war, much to Oswald's bitter regret, but it was denied any share in the emerging new era of jet propulsion, despite many attempts to break into that field with advanced - and original - designs of its own. The company was obliged to live from hand to mouth, taking in sub-contract work from other aircraft companies, and effectively becoming something of a "garage" for activities of all kinds, in a bid to keep employment up and skilled personnel active.

The resemblance to the situation after the First World War was extraordinary, the major difference being that now the company was nationalised and not free to follow its own inclinations, whereas Oswald post-1918 still had control of the company and could do as he pleased. Nevertheless, in the period from 1945 to 1979, despite the hardships, the company produced some outstanding innovative designs in both aircraft and missiles, and in aerostructures too, which contributed much to the overall development of aerospace.

It was Rear Admiral Matthew (later Sir Matthew) Slattery, appointed Managing Director in 1948, who was to lead Shorts through the immediate post-war years. His energy and fearlessness did much to help the company stay alive in the face of government indifference. He became Chairman in 1952, leaving the company in 1960 to become Chairman of BOAC.

Scraping the barrel. Desperate for work, Shorts, although under government ownership, were obliged to look everywhere for something to do. Products manufactured included milk churns (photographed here in 1948), carpet sweepers, and prefabricated aluminium-frame buildings.

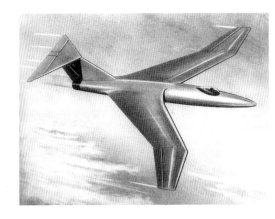

The company also
continued to demonstrate
its design flair, with radical
new ideas for aeroplanes
such as this. None, alas,
ever saw development, let
alone production.

One of the early post-
war aircraft was the
Sturgeon of 1946.
Although it was initially
conceived as a naval
reconnaissance bomber
(S-38), the design was
later substantially
changed to that of a
high-performance
carrier-based target-
towing aircraft (S-39)
and anti-submarine
aircraft (SB-3).

Flying-boat development and production were still going on. The Solent, shown here in the colours of British Overseas Airways Corporation, evolved from the S-45 Seaford (originally designated the Sunderland Mark IV), which first flew on 30 August 1944. At first intended for the RAF, which lost interest in it, the Seaford was adopted by BOAC for post-war flying-boat operations under the name Solent. Six Seafords were converted to Solents; 12 Solent 2s were built by Shorts for the airline, and four larger Solent 4s went to Tasman Empire

Airways. A Solent for BOAC was the last aircraft to be built at Rochester, in 1948, before the company became totally Belfast-based. Other earlier post-war Sunderland derivatives (from the Mark III) for BOAC and other airlines included the Hythe and Sandringham Classes. BOAC finally gave up flying-boat operations on 10 November 1950 (its last operation being a Solent flight from Johannesburg). On 5 May 1949, in celebration of 30 years of British civil air transport, a BOAC Solent alighted on the Thames to be named *City of London* by the Lord Mayor, Sir George Aylwen. The aircraft is seen here in the Pool of London, and moored opposite the Tower of London.

BOAC was still using converted Sunderlands on its
Empire service, like the Mark III pictured here in
Southampton Docks. But landplanes were becoming
more popular - the de Havilland Comet jet airliner,
the world's first, was already under development, as
was the Vickers Viscount turboprop airliner - and
BOAC began to run down its flying-boat activities.

The S-44/SA-6 Sealand twin-engined light commercial and military flying boat for five to seven passengers, was undoubtedly the most successful of Shorts early post-war ventures, making its maiden flight on 22 January 1948. Eventually 23 were built for various airlines and the Indian Navy, while two of a modified version went to Norway.

C.P.T. Lipscomb, who joined Shorts in 1914 and eventually became Technical Director before retiring in 1951. He continued to serve as a director of the company for some time thereafter.

Efforts to get into the landplane business, in the wake of the decline in flying-boat operations, were many and varied, and included the SA-4 Sperrin which was a four turbo-jet engined medium-range bomber - the company's only attempt at building a jet bomber of its own design. It flew on 10 August 1951. Two prototypes were built, but no quantity production order emerged.

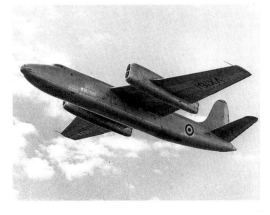

The SB-5 research aircraft, which made its maiden flight on 2 December 1952, was designed to study problems associated with the low-speed handling characteristics of swept-back wings, as part of the development programme for the projected English Electric P-1 Lightning supersonic fighter.

Three of Shorts' Chief Test Pilots: (Left) Geoffrey Tyson, who took over from John Lankester Parker in 1945. He left the company in 1946. (Centre) Harold Piper, who held the post from 1946 to 1948. (Right) Tom Brooke-Smith, Chief Test Pilot from 1948 until his retirement from active flying in 1960. During that period he played a major role in the development of vertical take-off and landing, one of the most advanced areas of aeronautical research.

The SB-4 Sherpa was another remarkable research venture. A single-seat aircraft, which first flew on 4 October 1953, it was intended to study the aerodynamic possibilities of what was called the "aero-isoclinic wing". But although Britain was moving into the supersonic era, helped by Shorts through their research activities, the company was to get no direct part with its own production designs.

David Keith-Lucas, whose fertile brain was responsible for many of the research aircraft produced by Shorts at this time. He served the company from 1940 to 1949 as Chief Aerodynamicist, then as Chief Designer (1949-58), Technical Director (1958-64), and as Director of Research (1964-65).

As a result of the Korean War in the early 1950s, the UK began a new rearmament programme, which improved the position for several major aerospace companies, including Shorts. One of the Shorts projects was production, under licence, of the English Electric Canberra twin-engined light bomber. Many versions were developed and in all Shorts built more than 130 Canberras of

various MKs, culminating in the high altitude photo-reconnaissance PR9 aircraft, which is still in service with the Royal Air Force today. Shorts also designed, developed and subsequently modified older B2 models for use as high altitude pilotless drone aircraft, which were used as targets in Britain's missile development programmes at the Woomera Range in Australia.

(Insert) Alex Roberts, Shorts PR9 Project Test Pilot in the late 1950s.

The SB-6 Seamew two-seat light anti-submarine aircraft made its maiden flight on 23 August 1953. But although an initial production order was placed for the Fleet Air Arm and RAF Coastal Command, no Seamews became operational.

Seamew test pilots Eric Hyde and Wally Runciman (far right).

Production of the Bristol Britannia long-range turboprop airliner was a major source of work during the 1950s. The first Shorts-built aircraft flew on 1 June 1957. Twenty-three Britannias were built for the RAF and 12 commercial versions for overseas airlines. Shown here is the aircraft and crew for the Canadian Pacific proving flight in April 1958, with test pilots Mike Ingle-Finch (front row left), Malcolm Wild (back row right) and Jock Eassie (far right).

One of the most challenging ventures during the 1950s was the SC-1 research aircraft, a true vertical take-off and landing (VTOL) flying test-bed. It was a follow-on from the earlier Rolls-Royce "Flying Bedstead" - an experimental VTOL test-rig. The first SC-1 prototype, piloted by Tom Brooke-Smith, first flew at the Government Aeroplane and Armament Experimental Establishment at Boscombe Down, Wiltshire, on 2 April 1957, and was the "star of the show" at the Farnborough Air Show in 1960 when "Brookie" retired from test flying. Subsequently Alex Roberts became Shorts SC-1 Project Test Pilot, being responsible for much of the development test flying which was carried out on the two SC-1 test aircraft through the Sixties, culminating in the successful demonstration of "transitions" using the full "fly by wire" control system specially developed for the aircraft by Shorts. (Left) Tom Brooke-Smith in front of the SC-1, with the Rolls-Royce Flying Bedstead alongside.

The price for exploring the frontiers of knowledge. An SC-1 crashed at Belfast on 2 October 1963, tragically killing its pilot, J.R. Green. He was trying to land his aircraft manually at Sydenham, Belfast, after a gyro failure: the aircraft rolled over onto its back within seconds of landing.

Philip (later Sir Philip) Foreman, who joined Shorts in 1958 to help develop the Seacat ship-borne guided missile programme. He eventually rose to become Chief Engineer, Chief Executive (in 1968) and then Chairman (on 1 April 1983), before retiring in 1988.

Thus for 30 years he was largely responsible for the extensive widening of the company's product range, and for exploiting to the full its emerging "triadic" structure as manufacturer of aircraft, guided missiles and aerostructures. He stands alongside Oswald Short as being one of the two great architects of the company's activities, together spanning 64 years of its history.

The Seacat missile was to prove one of the company's most successful products of the post-war years, selling widely both in the UK and overseas, and winning for Shorts the Queen's Award for Industry on a number of occasions. A land-based version, called the Tigercat, was developed from it and became highly successful with British and foreign armed forces.

Despite its many achievements in the late 1950s and early 60s, the company was still struggling to keep its labour force employed. Various activities were undertaken, including the manufacture of straddle carriers for lifting bulky loads - such as these elephants at Chipperfield's Circus in 1959 - and Nobel motor cars. Among other unlikely items produced by Shorts at this time were wheelchairs and laundry drying-racks.

Hugh Conway, who was Chief Engineer and later Managing Director of Shorts during the 1950s and up to 1964, when he joined the Bristol Engine Division of Rolls-Royce as Managing Director.

(Above) From 1961 to 1967, the company was guided as Chairman by a distinguished industrialist, C.E.("Denis") Wrangham (later knighted). He succeeded Sir Matthew Slattery.

Denis Tayler, who succeeded Tom Brooke-Smith as Chief Test Pilot in 1960, holding the post until he retired in 1969.

The SC-7 Skyvan was a private venture by Shorts, designed to capture a large share of an emerging market worldwide for a small, rugged, reliable and low-cost transport, especially in developing countries. Design began in 1959, and the maiden flight took place on 17 January 1963 with Denis Tayler at the controls. The aircraft was well received and 150 were sold, mainly for export, with production continuing until 1986.

The SC-5 Belfast heavy long-range strategic freighter, which made its maiden flight on 5 January 1964, was a major project for the company during the 1960s, although only 10 aircraft were built for the RAF before the programme was cancelled by the Government under a round of defence spending cuts. Later, during the 1970s, the Belfasts were withdrawn from RAF service, but several were sold to civil customers and remain in operation today.

Denis Haviland, a high-ranking civil servant and industrialist, who was a director of Shorts from 1964 to 1972, and served temporarily as Chairman in 1967-68 after the departure of Sir Denis Wrangham.

Air Marshal Sir Edouard Grundy, who took over the chairmanship in 1968 from Denis Haviland, remaining in the post until 1976.

7. A RISING TEMPO OF ACTIVITY

1970-1989

Through the 1970s and 80s, Short Brothers were busier than they had ever been across all their major areas of activity: aircraft, guided weapons and aerostructures.

But the going remained tough, for competition in world markets was fierce and the company was obliged to work hard to win customers. It succeeded by targeting a series of key niche sectors of the aerospace spectrum and, through the application of advanced technology, exploiting them with products of high quality, backed up by skilful and dedicated marketing.

Having designed and manufactured wings for the Dutch Fokker F28 twin-jet airliner, Shorts became risk-sharing partners with Fokker and Deutsche Airbus of Germany in the Fokker F100 programme. Shorts designed, developed and manufacture the wings for the aircraft, which first entered service in 1988.

Another major element of the expanding aerostructures business in the 1980s was the manufacture of nacelle systems and components for a wide range of turbofan aero-engines. These included the Rolls-Royce RB211-524 series of powerplants for the twin-engined Boeing 767 and four-engined 747, and the RB211-535 for the twin-engined Boeing 757. Other major nacelle customers included Textron Lycoming and their LF507 engines for the British Aerospace BAe146 four-engined airliner. In conjunction with Rohr Industries of the USA, Shorts were also involved in the design, development and manufacture of some 40 per cent of the nacelle for the International Aero Engines' V2500 A and D series of powerplants for the Airbus A320, A321 and (later) McDonnell Douglas MD90 airliners. Over many years, Shorts had established themselves as a major world source in this field, especially pioneering the use of lightweight advanced composite materials. Shorts are also building nose cowls for the Rolls-Royce Trent high-thrust engine (right).

The SD-330 was a major new aircraft venture by Shorts during the 1970s, following on from the experience with the smaller Skyvan. It made its maiden flight on 22 August 1974. With its flexible operational performance and proven reliability, it sold well in world markets as a commuter transport, and did much to promote the concept of short-haul commuter-type operations around the world.

Don Wright (left), who was appointed Chief Test Pilot in January 1969, retiring in December 1976. His successor was Lindsay Cumming (centre), who held the post until October 1984, when he in turn was succeeded by H.W.Allan Deacon (right). Tragically, Allan Deacon was killed whilst undertaking a test flight in a Tucano aircraft over the Irish Sea on 22 February 1991. He was 57.

Sir George Leitch, a prominent civil servant, who took over the chairmanship from Sir Edouard Grundy in 1976 and held the post until his own retirement in 1983. He was followed by Sir Philip Foreman, who for some time had been Chief Executive under Sir George.

The SD-360 twin-turboprop airliner was a major development of the 1980s. The 36-seat aircraft first flew on 1 June 1981, and subsequently won a sizable share of world commuter markets with over 150 being sold.

The company also found a new market with its Sherpa light military turboprop aircraft, derived from the 330 commuter transport. The initial multi-million-dollar order was for 18 Sherpas for the US Air Force in Europe, with the designation C-23A. In October 1988, Shorts were awarded a $60 million contract for 10 enhanced-performance Sherpas, designated C-23B, for the US Army's National Guard. Five of these aircraft served with US Forces during the Gulf War in 1991. A follow-on order for six C-23Bs was completed in 1992. The company is also providing a full range of logistic support packages for these aircraft.

The Blowpipe (above) is a supersonic shoulder-launched battlefield missile designed primarily for the protection of land forces against low-level air strikes. It represented a major breakthrough for the defence of infantry and has proved a great success, being used by many armies around the world.

Drawing on the expertise it had gained with the combat-proven Blowpipe, Shorts developed a new surface-to-air advanced supersonic, close-range, man-portable guided missile, the Javelin. Designed to engage the widest range of low level targets, it was capable of instant reaction to high speed aircraft or helicopter attacks. The Javelin first entered service with the Royal Marines and the British Army in 1984-85, and subsequently was adopted by several overseas military forces.

The Javelin led to the development of a new, more advanced missile, the Starstreak close air defence weapon. In December 1986, Shorts won a £225 million contract from the UK Ministry of Defence for the development, initial production and supply of the Starstreak, mounted on the Alvis Stormer vehicle, together with lightweight multiple launcher and shoulder-launched variants to meet the British Army's requirement into the 21st century. The US Army's Strategic Defence Command also awarded Shorts contracts in order to assess Starstreak technology against the short-range ballistic missile threat.

Seen here is the vehicle-mounted version of Starstreak.

Production of the Tucano basic trainer (which evolved from the original Brazilian Embraer company's design) was also well under way in the late 1980s to meet an order from the RAF for 130 aircraft. The order, worth £130 million, was won in March 1985 against fierce competition from British Aerospace and others.

Rodney Lund, who was appointed Chairman of Short Brothers by the British Government in April 1988, in succession to Sir Philip Foreman. It was his tough task to fight for the privatisation of the company as an entity, avoiding its break up by the Government. He was ultimately successful, ensuring the company's sale intact to the Canadian-based Bombardier corporation. He is a member of the post-privatisation Shorts Board of Directors.

Rodney Lund was assisted by Roy McNulty, who had joined Shorts in 1978 as Director of Finance and Administration. He became Deputy Managing Director in 1986 and Managing Director two years later, on Sir Philip Foreman's retirement.

Towards the end of the 1980s, Shorts recognised that the market for turboprop 360 airliners was declining, in the face of growing interest in the development of a new generation of faster, smoother, short-to-medium-haul "regional jet" airliners Accordingly, it initiated its own market studies, and began to prepare designs for a small, twin-engined jet airliner called the FJX.
(Below) A mock-up of the FJX at the 1988 Farnborough International Air Show.
(Right)) An artist's impression of the aircraft, skilfully depicted against a photographic background.

Cash for FJX development was difficult to acquire, either from the British Government, which still owned Shorts, or from other external investors. Also, potential competition seemed likely to be fierce. A famous Canadian company, Canadair, part of the Bombardier group, was already developing its own regional jet and discussions between the two companies took place to try and agree the development of a single product.
(Below) The Canadair Regional Jet in flight.

Alex Roberts was also a member of the team which steered the company through its change of ownership. Formerly one of Shorts' test pilots for many years, he led the company's sales and marketing operations through the 1970s and 80s, and was then appointed Deputy Managing Director to Roy McNulty. He is now Executive Vice-President of Shorts.

8. PRIVATISATION AND THE TAKEOVER BY BOMBARDIER

Shorts' interest in developing their own regional aircraft, the FJX, brought them to the attention of Bombardier Inc, owners of Canadair, who were developing a potentially competing product. This was about the same time that the British Government, as part of its programme of divesting itself of various state-owned interests, was seeking possible buyers for the company. The Government had already successfully restored two other major UK aerospace companies to the private sector - British Aerospace and Rolls-Royce - and saw no reason why it could not do the same with Short Brothers.

The battle for Shorts was fierce, with initially over 30 organisations around the world seeking further information about the company; but that list was quickly whittled down, first to six serious potential bidders, then two - Bombardier, a major Canadian mass transit and leisure vehicle manufacturing conglomerate, and a consortium comprising GEC of the UK and Fokker of The Netherlands. Bombardier was successful because it stressed that it wanted to develop Short Brothers as an entity within its own organisation.

On 4 October 1989 an agreement, involving a complex financial reconstruction of Shorts, was signed at Queen's Island, Belfast, by the Rt. Hon. Peter Brooke, Secretary of State for Northern Ireland, and Laurent Beaudoin, Chairman and Chief Executive Officer of Bombardier. It effectively achieved the "privatisation" of Short Brothers, which had been in government ownership since its controversial takeover in 1943.

Mr Beaudoin stressed his conviction that, by combining the resources and skills of Bombardier and Shorts, the growth of both companies would be promoted, opening the way to building a major force of global scope in the aerospace sector well into the 21st century.

"We are enthusiastic about this acquisition," he declared, "and we are committed to making a success of Shorts which has outstanding potential. We are also convinced that this transaction offers great opportunities for sharing our experience and know-how in technology and management to our mutual benefit.

"Acquiring Shorts fits into the dynamics of Bombardier's evolution in several ways. It considerably widens and strengthens our position in the aerospace sector while reinforcing Bombardier's readiness to meet the challenge of Europe 1992 and securing our presence in the world market.

"The association of Bombardier and Shorts is bound to put to work synergies which will not only ensure the growth of both enterprises but will benefit the Northern Ireland economy."

Mr Beaudoin also confirmed that Shorts would remain a single unit within the Bombardier group, retaining their identity and carrying on as an integrated design and production unit in Belfast. Moreover, he stressed Bombardier's determination to provide Shorts with the capital structure needed to ensure their growth.

"Let me emphasise that Shorts is in businesses we understand, businesses which require staying power, long-term commitment, a sound mix of technology, engineering and marketing drive, and foremost, a dedicated labour force prepared to work as a team that is ready, willing and able to win.

"You should also know that Bombardier is not in the business of making short-term financial gain. We choose carefully the type of operation to which we are going to allocate resources, and then devote the time and energy required to succeed. Shorts is decidedly a fitting partner in our company's development."

The Rt. Hon. Tom King, then Secretary of State for Northern Ireland, formally announcing on 7 June 1989 the selection of Bombardier Inc of Canada as the preferred purchaser of Short Brothers. With him is Laurent Beaudoin, Chairman and Chief Executive Officer of Bombardier (left). Behind them is Roy McNulty, then Managing Director, now President of Shorts.

The historic signing ceremony on 4 October 1989, with the Rt. Hon. Peter Brooke, Secretary of State for Northern Ireland, seated on the left, alongside Laurent Beaudoin. David Haggan, the then Chairman of the Factory Committee, representing the employees of Shorts, is standing behind them, next to Roy McNulty. At the moment of signing, a new era in the long history of Short Brothers began.

PART TWO

THE BOMBARDIER STORY

*"Bombardier, which celebrated a half-century
of technological, industrial and commercial progress in 1992,
has a promising future, provided we continue to show
the same innovative and entrepreneurial spirit
that was the driving force behind our founder's success."*

LAURENT BEAUDOIN
Chairman and Chief Executive Officer
Bombardier Inc

THE BOMBARDIER STORY

Bombardier Inc, of which Short Brothers are now an integral part, is a Canadian corporation engaged in design, development, manufacturing and marketing activities in the fields of motorised consumer products, transport equipment, and civil and military aerospace. Now one of the biggest transport and aerospace manufacturing conglomerates in the world, Bombardier employs around 32,000 people and has an annual business volume of over C$3 billion. More than 90 per cent of the company's worldwide sales are to markets outside Canada, with a high concentration in North America and Europe. It has a total backlog of orders worth well in excess of C$5 billion.

Bombardier was created by a French-Canadian entrepreneur and inventor, Joseph-Armand Bombardier, who was a born mechanic and owned a garage in the small town of Valcourt, in the province of Quebec.

It had always been Armand's dream to be able to build vehicles that would travel smoothly and swiftly over the deep snows which last for many months in the long Canadian winters. Initially the idea developed only slowly, as he experimented with "snowmobiles" based on existing car bodies, such as Fords and Dodges; but the pace of activity quickened when he devised his own traction techniques and built his own vehicle bodies.

The result was the B-7 snowmobile (B for Bombardier, 7 for the number of passengers it carried), which enjoyed great success in meeting the transport needs of a large snow-bound clientele, such as country doctors, taxi and bus owners, power companies, telephone companies and foresters. Armand closed the garage and in 1937 began building and selling his vehicle under the name of L'Auto-Neige Bombardier. The business was formally constituted as a limited company on 10 July 1942, as L'Auto-Neige Bombardier Limitée.

From then onwards, despite many vicissitudes, especially during the Second World War when restrictions on the use of motorised vehicles put civilian snowmobile production "on hold" (although there was production for military use), the Bombardier enterprise grew. This was in large part due to a series of clever inventions which progressively refined the snowmobile concept. When civilian production recommenced after the war, among the first vehicles on the market were the versatile B-12 snowmobile for passenger and cargo transport, mail delivery and ambulance work; and the C-18 which carried schoolchildren during the winter in several parts of Quebec and Ontario.

By 1948, L'Auto-Neige Bombardier's sales had reached C$2.3 million. But when the Quebec Government implemented snow removal policies in rural areas the following year, the snowmobile industry was hard hit, and Armand decided to expand his product line and seek new markets.

In the early 1950s, he introduced a line of industrial all-terrain vehicles for the mining, oil and forestry industries which included the Muskeg tractor, still sold today in modified versions throughout the world, and the J-5, the first tracked vehicle to be used in the forestry industry (it later gave birth to the smaller SW tractor, still in use for urban snow removal). During the same period, he also perfected a light tracked vehicle which led to the introduction, in 1959, of the first personal snowmobile, under the "Ski-Doo" brand name.

This revolutionised the company, and gave rise to a new sport - "Snowmobiling" - and a new industry producing the vehicles. Bombardier grew rapidly, maintaining its leadership of the snowmobile industry, despite the emergence of a large number of competitors. Sales soared from C$10 million in 1963-64 to C$200 million in 1971-72.

It was in the early 1960s that another major influence in the Bombardier story, Laurent Beaudoin, began to emerge. The son-in-law of Armand, having married Claire

Bombardier, he was called in by his father-in-law to help with a sawmill that was losing money. Laurent Beaudoin, a chartered accountant, turned the business round, and Armand sought further advice on his estate. Laurent's advice, for Armand to buy out his three brothers, Leopold, Alphonse and Germain, was accepted. In 1963, aged 25, Laurent Beaudoin became controller of L'Auto-Neige Bombardier. The following year Armand died of cancer, having seen his snowmobile dream come true. In 1966 Laurent Beaudoin was named President of L'Auto-Neige Bombardier, leading a team that saw a phenomenal boom in the snowmobile industry. In 1967 the company changed its name to Bombardier Limitée, and went public two years later.

The boom was not to last. The 1973 energy crisis, coupled with restrictive legislation and environmental concerns, dealt a hard blow to the snowmobile industry, shrinking the market from 500,000 units per year to around 100,000, and reducing the number of manufacturers from over 100 to just six, of which Bombardier was one. The annual North American market currently ranges from 120,000 to 130,000 units and is shared by four competitors, including Bombardier, which to date has produced over two million recreational snowmobiles.

Bombardier began to diversify in 1974. Under Laurent Beaudoin's direction the company moved into the rail transit field, with an order to supply 423 rail cars for the Montreal subway network. It was a field in which the company was to become dominant. Through an extensive series of company acquisitions, and shrewd manufacturing, marketing and licensing agreements, Bombardier strengthened its market position not only in North America, but in Western Europe too.

Today, Bombardier's widespread industrial activities are collected into separate groups, linked by a central Corporate office which masterminds the company's long-range planning strategy and overall financial management. The Transportation Equipment Group - North America (with plants in Canada, the United States and Mexico) and Bombardier Eurorail in Western Europe (which comprises companies in Austria, Belgium, France and the UK) manufacture a wide range of locomotives, freight cars, containers, passenger-train coaches, subway cars, self-propelled transit vehicles and light rail vehicles, monorails and unmanned "PeopleMovers", exporting them all over the world. Through an agreement with GEC Alsthom, Bombardier is responsible for the marketing and manufacturing of the French TGV high-speed train in North America. One of its current major programmes is the construction of the shuttle-train cars for the English Channel Tunnel.

The Motorised Consumer Products Group, with factories in Canada, Austria and Finland, is responsible for the manufacture of the Ski-Doo snowmobile and its companion, the Sea-Doo watercraft, along with other tracked vehicles and small engines for motorcycles, ultra-light aircraft and industrial applications.

The Capital Group provides financing for dealers and manufacturers across a range of product areas through Bombardier Credit and Bombardier Capital, while Bombardier Real Estate has the mandate of developing the company's real estate assets earmarked for new uses.

AEROSPACE

In December 1986, Bombardier took a major step forward in its expansion programme when it entered the aerospace industry through the purchase of Canadair. Founded in 1944, Canadair has built over 4,000 civil and military aircraft, including nearly 600 supersonic fighters. Its current product line includes the Challenger business jet, the CL-215T and CL-415 amphibious aircraft, and the new-generation 50-passenger Canadair Regional Jet.

The purchase of Short Brothers from the UK Government in October 1989 further widened Bombardier's aerospace and defence interests, and added significantly to its position in Western Europe.

This was followed swiftly, in June 1990, by the

acquisition of Learjet, the well-known US manufacturer of business jet aircraft. Then, in January 1992, Bombardier acquired de Havilland Canada (in partnership with the Government of Ontario), whose range of turboprop-powered regional airliners are operated worldwide. Both these acquisitions enabled Bombardier to broaden its North American base in the aerospace industry and to offer comprehensive lines of executive jet and regional aircraft.

Canadair, Learjet and de Havilland are now linked under the title of Bombardier Aerospace Group - North America. Shorts Group, responsible for the European operations, are formally known as Bombardier Aerospace Group - Europe.

AVIATION SYNERGY

There is considerable synergy in the widespread aviation interests of Bombardier. Through the four units - Canadair, de Havilland, Learjet and Shorts - Bombardier has developed a substantial niche not only in a wide range of jet-powered business aircraft, but also in short- and medium-haul regional jet and turboprop-powered airliners. Furthermore, the four units, each with long histories in aeronautical development, individually possess a vast range of other aeronautically-based skills: in guided weapons, unmanned aerial vehicles and aerostructures manufacture. Collectively, therefore, they form a powerful aviation group which ranks seventh among the world's airframe manufacturers in the civilian aircraft market, and provides competition worldwide to other aerospace industries in the military aircraft and missile sectors.

This fits in with Bombardier's "corporate mission", which is to be the leader in the countries where it operates and to be recognised internationally as a world-class designer, manufacturer and distributor of transport equipment and other products and services related to its technology. The company's long-term objective is to enlarge or adapt specific product lines as a means of strengthening its position in the market sectors in which it competes.

Thus, in the aeronautical field, Laurent Beaudoin points out that "business jets, regional aircraft and the manufacture of components for major engine and airframe manufacturers represent the three pillars of our progress in aerospace. Such diversification has given us greater staying power during difficult times, while allowing us to make the most of favourable market conditions as they emerge."

But he adds that Bombardier is always looking forward on a long-term basis, and that other alliances or acquisitions anywhere in the world are possible, "if we feel that it would help to make our business more profitable or solidify our position in the market-place...The most important thing for us is to maintain a product line that is very competitive."

The founder of Bombardier, Joseph-Armand Bombardier, who was born in Valcourt, Quebec, on 16 April 1907, and died there on 18 February 1964. In 1942, after running his own garage for many years and perfecting his tracked vehicles for travel on the snowbound roads of rural Quebec, he set up L'Auto-Neige Bombardier Limitée.

(Below) The B-12 of 1940. Used initially for military purposes, this 12-passenger vehicle was one of Joseph-Armand Bombardier's first commercial products after the Second World War. It was subsequently sold all over the world, and widely used to carry mail, transport students in rural areas and, later, to haul wood.

(Above) The B-7 snowmobile of 1937. This motorised tracked vehicle was Joseph-Armand Bombardier's first commercial success (B for Bombardier, 7 for the number of passengers it carried). It was characterised by its wood and steel body, later changed to aluminium. Most of the B-7's customers were doctors and funeral directors, along with taxi and bus operators, power and telephone companies, and foresters.

The BR-400+
Snowgroomer is used
extensively in many parts
of the world for levelling
snow on ski slopes and
snowmobile trails.

The first personal snowmobile, 1959. For 27 years
Joseph-Armand Bombardier had worked to produce a
one- or two-seater "personal snowmobile". Early in
1959, the first model of what was to be called the
Ski-Doo appeared. Weighing 330lb (150kg), it was
propelled by a 4-cycle Kohler engine and could reach
a maximum speed of 15mph (24km/h) on snow. This
model was to create a whole new sport called
"Snowmobiling", and give an unprecedented boost to
the snowmobile industry.

The Ski-Doo personal snowmobile is available in a range of models to suit the requirements of all types of customers. Pictured right is the Formula Mach Z model.

The Sea-Doo watercraft (XP model). The result of three years' research and development, the Sea-Doo watercraft was launched in 1987. Its superior performance has won it widespread recognition and it is rapidly increasing its market share not only in North America, but also in Europe, Latin America and Asia.

Choosing to diversify because of the downturn in the snowmobile market in the early 1970s, Bombardier entered the rail transit field. In 1974 the company won an order to build 423 rail cars for the Montreal subway system.

(Left) Shuttle-train cars for the English Channel Tunnel. Bombardier and its subsidiaries BN of Belgium and ANF-Industrie of France are members of the Euroshuttle consortium building the shuttle-trains for transporting buses (single level) and cars (double level) through the tunnel. Their joint contribution to this project is the design and manufacture of the rail cars.

(Above) The LRV 2000. Produced by Bombardier's Belgian subsidiary, BN, this light rail vehicle with a lowered floor is expected to meet urban transit needs for decades to come.

(Left) In 1982 Bombardier picked up one of the most significant orders ever in the rail equipment industry, with a contract to manufacture 825 steel-wheeled subway cars for the New York City Transit Authority.

An artist's rendering of the prospective TGV high-speed train proposed by Bombardier and its partner, GEC Alsthom, for the Quebec City-Windsor (Ontario) corridor.

(Left) The Mark VI Monorail, in revenue service at the Disney World resort in Florida, is the most heavily travelled passenger monorail system in the world.

(Right) Bombardier is designing and building a new generation of subway cars for Boston's Red Line, commissioned by the Massachusetts Bay Transportation Authority (MBTA).

Laurent Beaudoin, Chairman and Chief Executive Officer of Bombardier.

10. CANADAIR

Bombardier's first move into aviation was to acquire from the Canadian Government, in December 1986, Canadair, the famous builder of both military and civil aircraft. It was to be the start of a major programme of aerospace acquisitions which would eventually make Bombardier one of the biggest aircraft manufacturers in the world, especially in the fields of business jets and regional jet and turboprop airliners. Canadair production is spread among six plants in the Montreal area, and is part of the Bombardier Aerospace Group - North America.

Canadair's roots can be traced back to 1923, as the Aircraft Division of Canadian Vickers Limited, when it began to build amphibious aircraft to meet a demand for forest patrol and fire-fighting. This has remained a continuous business, culminating in today's CL-415 amphibious "water-bomber", capable of depositing 1,350 gallons (6,137 litres) of water and fire-retardant foam.

Canadair itself was created when Canadian Vickers ceded its aircraft operations to the Canadian Government in 1944. The first major programme at the company's new St Laurent factory was the wartime production of 369 twin-engined amphibious Canso maritime patrol aircraft. Derived from the famous US Consolidated PBY Catalina, some are still flying today, primarily being used for forest fire-fighting.

A long line of other civil and military aircraft followed the Canso, including transport versions of the British Bristol Britannia (which was also being built by Short Brothers): the CL-44-6 long-range transport for the Canadian Forces, and the CL-44D swing-tail freighter. A number of the latter are still in service. Another Britannia variant was the Argus, for long-range maritime patrol and anti-submarine warfare, shown here in exercises with a friendly submarine.

Innovation has always been Canadair's strongest suit, as demonstrated by (right) the CL-84 tilt-wing transport for vertical and short take-off and landing (VSTOL), and (below) the CL-227 Sentinel unmanned aerial vehicle for "spy in the sky" reconnaissance and other missions.

(Far left) Canadair's Military Aircraft Division facility at Montreal International Airport, Mirabel, Quebec, provides system engineering support and maintenance for the Canadian Forces' CF-18 fighter aircraft, among others. (Left) Manufacturing nose barrels for the US Navy F/A-18A combat aircraft.

Canadair also manufactures parts for larger commercial jet airliners, such as the Airbus A330/A340 (for which it also designed major fuselage components) and the Boeing 767 - for which it produces the rear fuselage section, including the pressure dome bulkhead shown here.

A major new turning point in Canadair's affairs
occurred in 1976, with the development of the
Challenger 600 business jet. The Challenger
represented a major technological advance, with its
wide fuselage, advanced technology airfoil, high-
bypass fan-jet engines, and sophisticated electronic
systems. The first flight occurred in 1978, with
certification and entry into service in 1980.

(Below) The Canadair Regional Jet in production at Montreal International Airport, Dorval, Quebec. The aircraft has already entered service, the first operator being Lufthansa's German subsidiary Lufthansa CityLine.

(Above) Experience with the Challenger led Canadair on to the development of yet another new concept, the Regional Jet - a twin-engined, 50-seat airliner, with a range of up to 1,620 nautical miles (3,000km) and a cruising speed of 528mph (850km/h).

Canadair is also designing a new executive jet aircraft, called Global Express, to fly further, faster and higher than any other business jet. With a cabin length of 48 feet (14.63m), the twin-engined Global Express will fly eight passengers more than 5,650 nautical miles (10,464km) in wide-body comfort and will have a maximum speed just under the speed of sound (Mach O.9).

At the Farnborough International Air Show in September 1992, Bombardier announced the formation of a new Business Aircraft Division to look after marketing, sales and product support for the Canadair Challenger and Global Express business jets.

11. LEARJET

The well-known executive jet manufacturer, Learjet, was acquired by Bombardier in 1990, significantly broadening Bombardier's North American aerospace base and enabling it to offer the most comprehensive line of executive jets available anywhere in the world today.

William ("Bill") Lear, one of the most famous names in American aviation, founded the Lear Jet Corporation in 1962, to build his own design for a small, economic executive jet that would transport businessmen around North America at airline jet speeds. Thus was laid the foundation for a major new aircraft manufacturing industry.

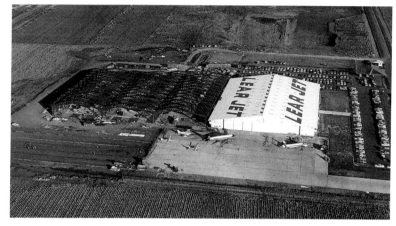

The first Lear Jet manufacturing plant under construction in Wichita, Kansas, in 1962. The business expanded rapidly, and the first aeroplane (designated Model 23) was followed by a succession of others as the concept of business jet aviation gathered momentum, not only in North America but worldwide.

The original Model 23 Learjet, which created a revolution in business air travel. But despite his aviation successes, Bill Lear was faced with a mounting financial crisis and, in 1967, reluctantly sold the controlling interest to Gates Rubber Company. In 1969, both the company and aircraft were renamed Gates Learjet. Bill Lear died in May 1978, by which time many hundreds of Learjets in different versions had been delivered throughout the world.

Among the most successful of Learjet's products has been the 35A, one of the world's most popular executive jets. Used for both business transport and special missions with armed forces (designated C-21A by the US Air Force), there have been well over 700 35s, and its long-range counterpart the 36, delivered to date.

A business jet photocall: (clockwise from lower left) Learjet 35A, Learjet 31, Canadair Challenger, Learjet 55C and Learjet 36A. To date, Learjet has built more than 1,675 business jets, and has accumulated over three billion miles in customer service.

In 1987, Integrated Acquisition Inc, a wholly owned subsidiary of Integrated Resources Inc, of New York, acquired Gates Learjet Corporation. The name was changed to Learjet Corporation, with the company continuing to manufacture executive jets. The picture shows the Learjet facilities in Wichita, amounting to over 1.2 million square feet (111,600sq.m). The plant is used not only for aircraft manufacture but also for aerospace sub-contract work for the US Space programme, Boeing and the US Air Force, as well as for maintenance, refurbishment and parts manufacture for Learjets in service.

The Learjet plant in Tucson, Arizona. Over 500,000 square feet (46,500sq.m) in area, it houses separate service centres for Learjets and the Canadair Challenger, along with refurbishment and completion facilities for these and other aircraft. A number of Learjets manufactured in Wichita are finished with interior fittings and exterior paintwork at Tucson, and returned to Wichita for ultimate delivery to customers.

Bombardier, which had already acquired Canadair in 1986 and Short Brothers in 1989, further expanded its aviation interests by purchasing the Learjet Corporation in June 1990. Canadair and Learjet, along with de Havilland, now form the Bombardier Aerospace Group - North America. The picture shows the final assembly line in Wichita, where all the Learjet models are manufactured. A large flight test centre there serves both Canadair and Learjet, and will be used by other Bombardier companies for the development of new aircraft.

The Learjet 60, seen on its maiden flight at Wichita in June 1991. The aircraft
was scheduled to receive its type certification in early 1993, clearing it for
customer service. This 533mph (858km/h) business jet can fly coast-to-coast in
the USA, with a range of 2,740 nautical miles (5,074km) with reserves, and can
operate from runways as short as 5,360 feet (1,633m). The largest business jet
yet built by Learjet, it is already winning orders worldwide.

12. DE HAVILLAND CANADA

The acquisition of de Havilland Canada was achieved in March 1992, bringing into Bombardier a long and successful line of short-haul turboprop regional airliners. As a result, through Canadair, Learjet and de Havilland, together comprising the Bombardier Aerospace Group - North America, Bombardier now has a powerful position in the world's executive jet, short-haul regional jet and turboprop airliner markets.

Formed as a limited company in 1928, as a sales and assembly arm for the British parent de Havilland Aircraft Company's products, "DHC", as it was popularly known, became a fully-fledged aircraft manufacturer in its own right in 1938. It began by building Tiger Moth trainers for the Royal Canadian Air Force, along with Menasco Moths, Mosquito bombers and Ansons for the war effort. Its first indigenous design was the DHC-1 Chipmunk trainer (below) in 1946, of which it built 217. A further 1,000 were built in England and 60 more in Portugal.

(Right) The tough, versatile DHC-2 Beaver of 1947 became one of de Havilland Canada's most famous aeroplanes, with 1,692 built in various versions including the Turbo-Beaver variant. As recently as 1987, 40 years after its first flight, the Beaver was selected as one of the top 10 Canadian engineering achievements of the past century.

(Opposite) The larger DHC-3 Otter first flew in 1951. It had double the payload of the Beaver and a greater range, and was used by operators in the Canadian North and other remote regions of the world. In all, 466 were produced.

In 1958 came the first flight of the DHC-4 Caribou Short Take-off and Landing (STOL) utility transport, of which 307 were built for military and civil operators. Soon afterwards, in 1961, DHC was taken over by the British group Hawker Siddeley, as part of their acquisition of the parent de Havilland company in the extensive UK aircraft industry rationalisation of that time.

The first twin turbine-engine powered de Havilland Canada aircraft was the outstanding DHC-5 Buffalo, which made its maiden flight in 1964. It set six speed-to-height records in a single flight, and was popular with armed forces round the world, who collectively bought 126 of the type.

The ubiquitous DHC-6 Twin Otter first flew in 1965. Designed as a utility bush aeroplane for the Canadian North, the Twin Otter found its true niche with the developing commuter airlines. It became the largest-selling 19-passenger commuter aircraft in the world, with 844 ordered, and was instrumental in developing the regional airline industry as we know it today. Many are still in service worldwide. (Left) A Twin Otter variant used by the British Antarctic Survey.

In 1974 de Havilland Canada was sold by Hawker Siddeley to the Canadian Government. By that time the company was heavily involved in developing its first major regional short take-off and landing (STOL) airliner, the turboprop Dash 7. With 113 built, the Dash 7 has been instrumental in pioneering unique operational techniques at major airports requiring steep-angle approaches, most recently in the development of the London City Airport in Docklands.

(Right) In 1983 the 37-40 passenger Dash 8 Series 100 aircraft made its maiden flight, leading the way in the development of new-generation turboprop regional airliners around the world.

(Left) In 1986 the US company Boeing acquired de Havilland Canada from the Canadian Government. Soon after that deal, Boeing announced the go-ahead for the stretched Series 300 version of the Dash 8, seating 50-56 passengers. The first derivative in the Dash 8 family of aircraft, it entered service in 1989.

In March 1992, Bombardier purchased de Havilland Canada in corporate partnership with the Government of Ontario. Bombardier holds 51 per cent in the new company, de Havilland Inc, the Ontario Government 49 per cent. Shortly afterwards, de Havilland launched the Series 200 version of the Dash 8 turboprop airliner. Identical in size to the Dash 8 Series 100, it has a higher cruise speed and greater range and payload, enabling airlines to increase flight frequencies or to extend their operational radius.

At the 1992 Farnborough International Air Show, Bombardier announced the establishment of a Regional Aircraft Division as part of its North American aerospace group, to undertake the marketing, contracts and in-service support of both the Canadair Regional Jet and the de Havilland Dash 8 twin turboprop family of aircraft (pictured here together). Manufacturing of the Regional Jet and Dash 8 continues to be the responsibility of Canadair and de Havilland respectively.

PART THREE

SHORTS ENTER A NEW ERA

*"It is the people of Shorts who are
making changes happen and repaying
Bombardier's faith in us."*

ROY MCNULTY
PRESIDENT OF SHORT BROTHERS PLC

SHORTS ENTER A NEW ERA

Shorts today are a very different company from that acquired by Bombardier in 1989. In the period since then, not only has the company undergone many physical changes as a result of the £200 million four-year investment programme in new plant, machinery, equipment and facilities, but there has been a major "cultural revolution" throughout the entire organisation affecting both the way it is run and its outlook at all levels of the workforce. Whilst special emphasis is being placed upon "customer focus" - ensuring that the customer comes first in everything that Shorts undertake - this revolution also encompasses new organisational structures and, especially, new working practices, embodying the key concept of "Total Quality".

The objective has been, and continues to be, the regeneration of Shorts as a major force in international aerospace, capable of competing and operating profitably in the increasingly fierce commercial and industrial environment that already prevails and will continue into the new century. In brief, Shorts have become - and intend to remain - a World Class Performer.

Changing market situations throughout the world aerospace industry in the late 1980s, including rising costs, increased product complexity and tougher competition, had already forced new management and operational techniques on many other major companies in the US, UK and elsewhere, leading to greater concentration on international collaboration. This situation had not been lost on the management of Shorts, which undertook its own studies into how to cope in the tougher world aerospace business climate that was emerging, and was beginning to implement them.

But it was the British Government's decision in 1988 to privatise the company that really created the opportunity for rapid change. Once privatisation had been achieved, with Shorts becoming part of the Bombardier Group, the company's "Project 2000" programme, embodying new organisational changes, new core management practices and new standards of personal performance, responsibility and accountability, could be accelerated.

Supported by the availability of the £200 million investment capital, the turn-round strategy - to be implemented over a four-year period and fuelled by a new "bottom-line orientated" management philosophy - included:

● the focus on new strategic business units within the company, each covering a different product activity;

● the decentralisation of managerial responsibility, with a reduction in the number of different management layers so as to enhance personal responsibility and accelerate decision-taking;

● improved leadership by management at all levels, accompanied by greater decentralisation and flexibility in labour relations, and greater emphasis upon developing the talents of the workforce, especially the younger people;

● modernisation of plant, machinery and buildings throughout the company, with a complete review of layouts and work-flows;

● concentration upon immediate problems such as solving a parts shortage on various products, and eliminating schedule delays;

● ending production of the SD-360/Sherpa aircraft programme (whilst continuing to support those aircraft already in service), and finding a major programme to replace them;

● increasing exports of Javelin missiles;

● completing the Starstreak missile development programme and exploiting its potential.

The stated overall mission of this programme was, and remains today, "to achieve leadership in each sector of our business by continuously improving the company's products and operations to meet customers' needs and surpass our international competitors."

The company is convinced that this objective can be achieved only by adhering to three basic principles:

Total Quality and recognition of the overriding importance of

technical excellence - Shorts products must be the best;

Personal motivation - the necessity to use to the full the skills and energies of every employee: people *are* the key to the company's success. Talents in every field are being nurtured and put to full use by creative training and management, and the introduction of state-of-the-art equipment;

The recognition of cost-effectiveness as essential at all levels of operation - profits are the measure of the company's success.

Basic to all of these principles is the principle of complete integrity in every aspect of the business: the need for continuous improvement in performance at all levels of the company, calling for increased innovation, teamwork and employee involvement, and for closer working partnerships with suppliers, leading to total customer satisfaction.

Already, this revitalisation programme, unsurpassed in scope and extent in the company's history, is ensuring new levels of customer satisfaction and immeasurably enhancing Shorts' competitiveness in all the markets they serve.

This is being reflected in financial terms. Employment is up some 10 per cent to around 8,500, annual turnover has doubled to around £400 million in 1991-92, and a 1988 loss of £47 million was turned into significant profits in 1990-91 and 1991-92.

In 1992, Shorts were presented with the British Quality Award in recognition of the company's success "in implementing Total Quality in products and processes, involving all employees, achieving a significant change in culture, resulting in continuous improvement and increased customer satisfaction."

This is the premier British award in the Quality arena and previous winners have included Ford, IBM, Rank Xerox and Sony. Total Quality projects, in which the majority of Shorts' workforce have been involved, have resulted in cost savings of over £35 million by the end of 1992, in improved quality and competitiveness of products, and in much greater customer satisfaction. Shorts plan to extend involvement in quality projects to all their workforce because experience demonstrates that the contribution they make can help greatly in the growth and success of the company.

Shorts believe that the achievement of these aims is necessary not only for the company's future profitability and security in world markets, but is essential for the long-term prosperity and political and social stability of the community in which it is established.

As the largest private-sector employer in Northern Ireland Shorts occupy a unique position in the province, and are very conscious of their responsibilities to all sectors of the community. The decline of many of the province's more traditional engineering industries over recent years has served to accentuate that position. The result is that Shorts are deeply committed to making a positive contribution to the regional economy of Northern Ireland, and to being a good corporate citizen and neighbour.

This is being achieved through the active encouragement of local companies and businesses to become quality-approved suppliers to Shorts; a move which is already showing beneficial results throughout the province.

It is also being supported through the strong links which the company has created with local education establishments and training organisations. In these areas, Shorts' activities embrace young people from primary school to university levels. They range from sponsoring school projects to endowing the Shorts Chair of Aerospace Engineering at Ulster's oldest university - and they involve all sections of the community.

The evident result of the events and activities of the past few years is the new sense of achievement and motivation through-out the organisation. Shorts teams working in every sector of the business are headed by men and women who believe in the concept of committed and enlightened management. It is they who are leading their teams in a radically different environment based upon decentralisation of management, greater worker participation, improved communications, new long-term wage agreements, new capital investment, and emphasis on Total Quality. Shorts' aim is to ensure that change is seen to be working for the benefit of all.

13. WIDENING THE INDUSTRIAL BASE

The position of Shorts as a major force in world aerospace is illustrated by their role within Bombardier and by the new international liaisons they are forging with other aerospace companies.

Centred on the 480-acre complex of Queen's Island near the heart of Belfast (the company also has subsidiary offices in London, Bahrain, Washington and Hong Kong), Shorts employ some 8,500 personnel. In addition to Queen's Island, there are manufacturing and other facilities at Newtownards, Newtownabbey, Dunmurry and Castlereagh, all in Northern Ireland. The Group includes the rapidly expanding Belfast City Airport, less than 10 minutes' drive from the city's business centre.

Among recent acquisitions is the former Learfan aircraft factory at Newtownabbey, County Antrim, extending the company's advanced composites facilities supplying Shorts' main aerostructures assembly lines. Shorts are now a Centre of Excellence for advanced composites manufacture within Bombardier. Shorts have also become a substantial minority shareholder in Maydown Precision Engineering of Londonderry. Their considerable investment in the company has led to a significant increase in Maydown's workforce and its ability to supply machined components for Shorts' assembly lines.

To facilitate the new objectives laid down after the acquisition by Bombardier, the industrial base of Shorts has been restructured into five main autonomous business units - the Manufacturing, Aircraft, Defence Systems, Fokker, and Nacelle Systems Divisions - each of which has a strong customer focus and is responsible for a separate part of the broad product and service range which makes up the overall business of the company.

Augmenting these activities is a supporting corporate organisation that includes a central engineering group with research, development and test facilities, an information technology service and a corporate finance function - as well as personnel, training, corporate marketing, public affairs, security and other departments. The corporate organisation acts as co-ordinator and back-up for the five specialist business units. To this end, it employs specialist teams in many scientific and technical disciplines, whose services are available to business unit managements.

The corporate organisation plays an essential role in ensuring that the company's resources are employed selectively, efficiently and cost-effectively in the service of customers. It is also responsible for the company-wide Total Quality programme which is today fostering the advancement of the high product standards for which Shorts have always been renowned, even reaching back to the days of the three founders.

A concentrated drive in manager training and development, initiated at the very start of the restructuring programme, has resulted in the establishment of a management force which is providing the leadership needed for the transformation of the company.

Shorts President Roy McNulty being presented with the 1992 British Quality Award by the Rt. Hon. Michael Heseltine MP, President of the Board of Trade, on 11 November 1992.

This is the largest of the five new business units, employing more than 2,000 personnel. It serves as the premier parts supplier for the company's civil and military aircraft and aerostructures operations, and, as such, plays a fundamental role in their production programmes.

The division is also responsible for assembling the complete range of major airframe components for which Shorts are sole-source suppliers to Boeing. This includes main landing gear doors for the 747, wing flaps (including carbon-fibre components) for the 757, and the all-composite rudder assemblies for the 737 - the world's best-selling jet airliner, with over 3,000 ordered to date. Shorts will also supply nose landing gear doors for Boeing's new 777 twin jet.

The division's activities involve an impressive range of processes - some demanding extensive clean-air facilities - and a remarkable variety of components, covering almost every aspect of aircraft manufacture.

Shorts' on-going modernisation involves a substantial programme of investment in the division, providing advanced plant and equipment to ensure the cost-effective, on-time supply of high quality components. As a result, Shorts are now one of the world's most advanced aerospace manufacturers, with some of the most technically sophisticated machine tools.

Boeing has been a major Shorts' customer for nearly 20 years, and Shorts are currently sole-source supplier for the all-composite rudder of the 737 (left), the undercarriage doors for the 747, and the inboard trailing edge flaps for the 757. Shorts are also involved in another major programme for Boeing: the manufacture of nose landing gear doors for the new medium-to-long-range 777 (above) - the world's largest twin-engined jet airliner, due to make its first flight in 1994.

Shorts have been manufacturing major composite components for over two decades, and have recently modernised and substantially increased capacity to meet growing worldwide demand. The company's Composite Production Unit is now one of the most advanced of its kind in the industry and has been established as the Centre of Excellence for composite components within the Bombardier group. The work of the unit is carried out at two separate sites - at Newtownabbey and Dunmurry.

The Boeing 737 rudder (shown here), measuring 21 feet (6.4m), is one of the largest composite components fitted to any modern aircraft. The rudder structure is over 90 per cent carbon fibre with a composite spar and a honeycomb skin construction.

The control room of the autoclave section in which metal components are bonded under extreme heat. The circular door of one of the autoclaves can be seen in the background behind the controller.

Part of the vast, refurbished machine-shop in the division's main Belfast complex.

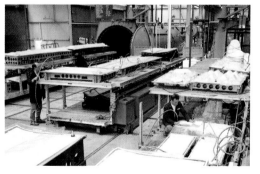

Carbon composite components being unloaded from an autoclave at Newtownabbey.

Operating in both the military and civil markets, the Aircraft Division is one of the most advanced design and production units of its kind anywhere in the world.

On the commercial side, since the mid-1960s, the company has concentrated on short-haul aircraft activities - first with the famous Skyvan light aircraft, followed in the 1970s by the 30-seat 330 regional airliners, and then by the larger 36-seat 360. Freighter aircraft have included the 330-UTT tactical transport, the 330 civil freighter, the multi-role civil Sherpa, the C-23A Sherpa for the US Air Force and the C-23B variant for the US Army National Guard. In all, around 450 of these aircraft have been built, and their logistics and other support remain a major function and source of income for the Aircraft Division.

Today, Shorts are involved in the new era of regional airliner development, playing a major role in the design and manufacture of the 50-seat Canadair Regional Jet, which entered airline service in the autumn of 1992. The division has responsibility for the aircraft's 32ft-long (9.75m) main fuselage barrel section, including the

forward and aft fuselage extension plugs, as well as the wing-mounted flight control surfaces - flaps, ailerons, spoilers and spoilerons, and the design of the vanes. The contract is for an initial quantity of 400 ship-sets, although this number may well rise as the aircraft continues to win worldwide acclaim.

Shorts are also a major partner with Learjet and de Havilland in the new Learjet 45 business jet, announced in September 1992. Shorts are responsible for the design and manufacture of the complete fuselage, and the manufacture of the empennage, for this 8-10 seat business jet which will establish new standards in passenger comfort, performance, maintainability, extended warranty and value.

The Canadair RJ entered service with Lufthansa CityLine, a regional airline subsidiary of the German flag carrier, in autumn 1992, and has won increasing acclaim from the airline and passengers alike.

Work on fuselage barrel production for the Canadair Regional Jet.

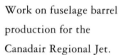

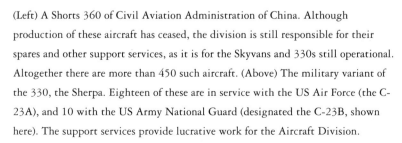

(Left) A Shorts 360 of Civil Aviation Administration of China. Although production of these aircraft has ceased, the division is still responsible for their spares and other support services, as it is for the Skyvans and 330s still operational. Altogether there are more than 450 such aircraft. (Above) The military variant of the 330, the Sherpa. Eighteen of these are in service with the US Air Force (the C-23A), and 10 with the US Army National Guard (designated the C-23B, shown here). The support services provide lucrative work for the Aircraft Division.

One of 16 Tucano basic trainers ordered by the Kuwait Ministry of Defence. The high-performance turboprop is being used to train student pilots for the Kuwait Air Force. The Tucano export version incorporates advanced modifications, including enhanced avionics, improved air conditioning (for warm climates), and the option of carrying external stores. It provides an excellent platform for weapon training and offers a highly effective counter-insurgency capability.

Late in 1992 Shorts won a major contract from Learjet to design and manufacture the complete fuselage, and to build the empennage (tail-plane), for the new Learjet 45 business jet aircraft (below). This is a medium-size, twin-engined aircraft designed to carry 8-10 passengers over distances of some 2,200 nautical miles (4,074 km). Work on this new venture is already well under way at Shorts, with certification of the aircraft set for 1996. When in full production, the Learjet 45 will provide an additional 700-800 jobs at Shorts. Another Bombardier Aerospace-North America company, de Havilland, will be responsible for the wings. Aircraft assembly and programme management will be undertaken by Learjet at Wichita.

Shorts' magnificent men minus their flying machines: (Sitting, left to right) Stephen Gillan (co-pilot); Dick Manning (test pilot); Dave Reid (chief pilot); Dave Pullan (pilot); Stephen Mills (co-pilot).
(Standing, left to right) Paddy Crowther (chief pilot, training and military aircraft); Bill Holloway (senior co-pilot); Simon Healy (chief pilot, commercial and communication aircraft).

Shorts offer a full range of back-up services from basic engineering and inventory support to full contract logistic support at customers' sites. The company has contracts to support the C-23B Sherpas in operation with the United States Army National Guard, and the C-23A Sherpas located at Edwards Air Force Base in California. Shorts staff provided direct support for five C-23B Sherpas in Operation Desert Storm, and were commended for their quick deployment response and "outstanding performance in the theatre of operations".
The company also has contracts to support the RAF Tucano, covering the operation of over 100 aircraft at four stations. At RAF Finningley, Shorts maintain seven different aircraft types and provide all other engineering and logistic services for the base.

Shorts' Defence Systems Division leads the world in close air defence guided weapons.

Since the early 1960s, when its Seacat ship-to-air missile entered service with the Royal Navy (to be adopted later by 15 other naval forces), the division has specialised in the close-range missile field. Its shoulder-launched Blowpipe achieved outstanding success in the Falklands Campaign and became a best-seller.

It was followed, in 1984, by the equally successful Javelin, adopted by armed forces worldwide; and then in 1991 by the advanced Starburst ground-to-air defensive missile system, developed from the Javelin. The Starburst is the most effective weapon of its kind currently in service, providing front-line air defence for the British Army. It performed excellently during the Gulf War. These three missile systems are class leaders, already selected by nearly 50 armed forces in over 30 countries.

The division's latest development, the high-velocity Starstreak, adds a completely new dimension to close-range missile technology. Capable of destroying any type of helicopter or fixed-wing ground attack aircraft, it delivers a lethal three-dart warhead at several times the speed of sound, and is immune to all known counter-measures.

Starstreak in the self-propelled mode, plus shoulder-launch and multiple launcher systems, has already been chosen to meet the British Army's close air defence requirements into the next century. The company has been awarded a £225 million contract from the UK Ministry of Defence for design, initial production and supply of these weapons mounted on the Alvis Stormer vehicle, together with lightweight multiple launcher and shoulder-launched variants.

The division is collaborating with McDonnell Douglas Helicopters on the adaptation of Starstreak to the Apache light-attack helicopter for air-to-air roles; and is working with Boeing on its development as a companion to the heat-seeking Stinger missile on the Boeing Avenger high-mobility weapon system, now in service with the US Army. A ship-borne version of the missile (Seastreak) has been specifically designed to provide surface vessels with a potent defence against "stand-off" anti-ship missiles and low-level strike aircraft.

In addition to its missile programmes, the Defence Systems Division markets a range of armoured security vehicles. The Shorland, based on a strengthened 110-inch (2.8m) Land-Rover chassis, has been exported to some 40 countries. Also in production is a range of target drones, including the subsonic Skeet and supersonic Stiletto, which provide cost-effective aids in operator training and weapon-firing trials.

In June 1991, Shorts and Thomson-CSF of France signed a "memorandum of understanding" to lead to the joint development of a new generation of Close Air Defence (CAD)/ Very Short Range Air Defence (VSHORAD) missile systems. Shorts have also signed an agreement with Spartanics of the USA

(Left) The laser-guided Starburst close air defence missile system, being fired in its lightweight multiple launcher (LML) mode in Saudi Arabia. Now in service with the British Army, Starburst was developed from the highly successful Javelin missile, but incorporating much advanced technology. The weapon system can also be deployed in shoulder-launch, armoured vehicle mounted and naval multiple launch modes.

jointly to market, develop, manufacture and support weapon simulation and training devices. In September 1992, Shorts and Spartanics announced a new product, the S-1 Multi Arms Trainer, designed to give forces a cost-effective alternative to firing-range training.

The new missile production centre at Castlereagh, Belfast, is one of the most modern guided weapons design, development and manufacturing centres in the world. The picture shows the advanced clean air facilities in which work is undertaken.

Combining state-of-the-art technology with combat-proven design features, Starstreak is the most effective weapon of its kind. It gives ground forces quick-reaction protection against high-speed strike aircraft, and offers a lethal defence against helicopter attack. (Above) Lightweight multiple launcher mode. (Right) Shoulder-launch mode. (Below) Self-propelled mode, mounted on a Stormer armoured vehicle.

(Below) The Skeet aerial target drone being launched. The Skeet has been in service with the British Army since 1982 and is used, among other roles, for practice firings of the Shorts Javelin and Starburst missiles. An improved version, the Mark 2, incorporates a more powerful engine and major waterproofing of the electronics to permit easy re-use after recovery from the sea.

(Above) Seastreak, the ship-borne variant of Starstreak, designed to provide surface vessels with a potent defence against "stand-off" missiles and low-level strike aircraft.

The S-1 Multi Arms Trainer, developed by Shorts and Spartanics of the USA, provides weapons training, both on a marksmanship (how to shoot) and scenario (when to shoot) basis, via a wide-screen video simulation system. Bringing together the innovative designs of both companies, it is capable of being used for training on a wide range of weapons from small arms to anti-tank missiles. It offers a realistic, cost-effective and environmentally-safe alternative to training on live firing-ranges, providing a highly flexible approach to the various requirements of armed forces and security agencies worldwide. The system is modular, and can be configured to suit individual customer requirements.

(Right) The Shorland range of armoured vehicles is primarily designed for use in internal security and law enforcement roles. The vehicle has proved a great success, with sales to more than 40 countries. The four variants in the Shorland Series Five are the S-52 Armoured Patrol Car, the S-53 Air Defence Vehicle, the S-54 Anti-Hijack Vehicle and the S-55 Armoured Personnel Carrier.

Shown here is the S-53, with the S-55 behind it.

Shorts have been for many years a major world source of high-technology aerostructures, including the design and manufacture of engine nacelle systems and components. The Nacelle Systems Division was formed to concentrate the company's acknowledged expertise in this high-technology market sector.

Based in the company's main Belfast complex, the division has produced to date well over 2,000 nose cowls for various versions of the Rolls-Royce RB211 engine used on Boeing 747, 757 and 767 airliners, and proposed for the Tupolev 204. The company is now involved in the design and manufacture of nacelle nose cowls, for the new high-thrust Rolls-Royce Trent engine for the Airbus A330 high-capacity airliner.

Other nacelle systems contracts include the design, development and manufacture of some 40 per cent of the nacelle (in partnership with Rohr Industries) for International Aero Engines' V2500 engines for the Airbus A320 and A321, and the McDonnell Douglas MD90. Shorts nacelle components have also been selected for the BMW Rolls-Royce GmbH BR700 range of aero engines. The company also produces complete nacelles for the Textron Lycoming turbofan engines used on the British Aerospace BAe146.

An important aspect of the division's work programme is its pioneering role in the increasing use of advanced, weight-saving composites. Shorts are among the industry's leading exponents of the use of composites in nacelle manufacture.

(Above) Rolls-Royce RB211 Trent engine with nacelle. Shorts and the French company Hurel-Dubois are responsible for major nacelle components for the engine, selected for the Airbus A330. Shorts designed and manufacture the nose cowl and engine build unit parts; Hurel-Dubois manufacture the thrust reverser. Through a separate entity (SINT) the companies are setting up a podding facility at Toulouse.

IAE's V2500 engine has already proved highly successful on the short-to-medium-range Airbus A320 (above), and has now been selected for the larger A321 and MD90 airliner (left).

Shorts manufacture the complete nacelles for the Textron Lycoming LF507 turbofans used on British Aerospace Regional Jetliners (above), as well as nacelles for the Canadair Regional Jet (top) and Challenger business jet.

The Russian Tupolev TU-204 shown landing at the Farnborough Air Display in September 1992, powered by Rolls-Royce RB211-535 engines with nacelle components manufactured by Shorts.

A major element of Shorts' present activities is their wing production contract for the Fokker 100 twin-engined jet liner programme, in which it is involved as part of a risk-sharing partnership with both Fokker of The Netherlands and Deutsche Aerospace of Germany.

In addition to their production commitment, Shorts were responsible for the design of the Fokker 100's high-reliability wing, which embraces the use of advanced composites to achieve weight-saving and reduce manufacturing costs.

The close association between Fokker and Short Brothers began in the mid-1960s, when Shorts became a risk-sharing partner in the earlier F-28 Fellowship twin-engined airliner project. Here too the company had responsibility for design, development and manufacture of the aircraft's wings, with over 240 wing-sets being delivered from Belfast before the end of F-28 production dovetailed with the establishment of the advanced Fokker 100 line.

The Fokker 100 first entered airline service with Swissair, the launch customer, in 1988, and production of wing-sets has continued at an accelerating pace to match the growth in the Fokker order book. Well over 200 wing-sets have been delivered to date. Fokker is now planning the launch of another short-haul jet airliner, the Fokker 70, with Shorts again as wing manufacturer.

Work at Belfast on Fokker 100 wings.

Shorts are providing the wings for the new Fokker 70
twin-engined 70-seat short-haul aircraft, which made
its maiden flight in spring 1993. It is part of a family
of airliners which includes the already successful
Fokker 100 and a projected, larger, Fokker 130.

BELFAST CITY AIRPORT

Short Brothers' main plant at Queen's Island, on the shore of Belfast Lough, is alongside the runway of Belfast City Airport, which the company owns and operates.

Officially opened for commercial business in February 1983, Belfast City Airport has expanded steadily and serves an increasing business and leisure clientele with scheduled services to many cities in the UK. It has an annual passenger throughput of around 600,000. The airport is fully equipped and staffed to the highest professional standards. It has benefited from a programme of continuous upgrading, to meet the demands of network expansion by user airlines, affecting all aspects of operation from passenger amenities to carrier services.

The airport is less than 10 minutes' drive from the heart of the city, which has a population of half a million.

An aerial view of Short Brothers (left and bottom left) and Belfast City Airport. The airport terminal can be seen centre right of the picture, near the bridge over the dual carriageway.

14. SERVING THE COMMUNITY

Shorts' role in the community as the biggest private employer and largest manufacturing company in Northern Ireland - aside from promoting closer business relationships with smaller companies in the province - has focused on the creation and maintenance of strong links with local educational establishments and training organisations.

The range of the company's activities spans primary school to university level, not just as a prospective source of future personnel, but as part of the process of widening local community awareness about the vital role the company plays in maintaining economic stability in the province.

One noteworthy contribution has been the endowment, in November 1989, of the Shorts Chair of Aerospace Engineering at Queen's University, Belfast. The objective is to ensure that the university, and the province itself, are recognised worldwide as a centre of excellence in aerospace engineering.

In addition to many individual school initiatives in which the company is involved, including school visits, work experience, work shadowing and careers conventions, Shorts have developed three major "outreach" programmes targeting young people.

"Flight", an educational aid package distributed to all 1,000 primary schools in Northern Ireland, as well as to schools in the Isle of Man, England and Wales, is aimed at children aged 10-11. It introduces them to the world of aerospace, and Shorts' contribution to its development.

"On The Wing", for second level secondary/grammar school pupils of 12-14, moves deeper into the technology of flight and the company's role in that technology. It is being followed by a more advanced programme for 16- to 17-year-olds, which familiarises students with aeronautical engineering and gives them a broader appreciation of aircraft technology, with an eventual career in aerospace in mind.

Many pupils have vague or perhaps stereotyped images of what it is like to work in industry, and so Shorts have always treated visits by schools as an important part of their education programme. Over 30 visits are made to the company by post-primary and third level colleges during any one year. Besides being an enjoyable experience, these give the students a first-hand insight into industrial activity.

In addition, Shorts have an intensive programme of career conventions throughout the province during the academic year. Managers from Shorts' Human Resources Department, and from other disciplines in the company, attend conventions and answer queries on entry requirements and career opportunities.

Work experience at Shorts is proving very popular with post-primary school students. One of the main attractions for young people is the "hands on" experience in an industrial working environment. On successful completion of their visit, students are awarded a Shorts "Industrial Certificate of Merit", and an assessment sheet is completed by the local manager and sent to the school. The students are also asked to complete a questionnaire giving their impressions of their time at Shorts.

Over recent years, Shorts have been a frequent winner of National Training Awards - in effect the UK's industrial "Oscars" awarded by the Government to organisations which have delivered exceptionally effective training programmes. The awards are fiercely contested throughout British industry. Shorts won an award in 1989 for its company-wide Total Quality programme, and again in 1990 for its Executive Potential Management Development programme (EXPO) for the development of young managers. In 1991, the company won a further award for its Aircraft Division's successful change from traditional working methods on unpressurised airframe structures in the Shorts 330 and 360 aircraft series to high-technology work on pressurised circular fuselage sections for the Regional Jet.

Shorts are dedicated to ensuring that, as equal opportunity employers, the economic benefits of its success under the Bombardier banner will spread far and wide throughout the community. The management and all personnel are determined that the company will play a major role in providing jobs, brighter prospects and a better future for all the people of Northern Ireland.

To support its various educational activities, Shorts produce a wide range of attractive and informative posters, books and pamphlets, some of which are shown below.

The "Flight" project, designed to introduce primary schoolchildren to the world of aerospace, has been enthusiastically received. Here pupils at Our Lady of Lourdes School, Belfast, learn about the principles of flight from Brian Carlin, Shorts Vice-President of Human Resources.

Members of the Belfast City Airport fire service pulling a 13-tonne Shorts 360 airliner along the one-and-a-quarter-mile runway in November 1991, to raise money for the BBC's "Children In Need Appeal". The firemen, through their individual sponsors, raised £1,500.

Shorts strongly encourage the families of its workforce to take an interest in the company's activities. At the Family Open Day in November 1991, young people got the chance to try their skills at the workbench, among other tantalising projects.

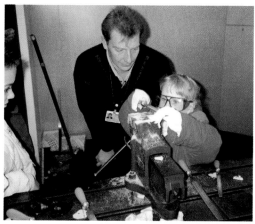

Shorts junior test pilots on the "Flight"
project - flying into the future.